HOW TO

NC

TRANSISTORS

A Self-Instructional Programed Manual

*This programed
learning text
has been prepared
under the direction of
C. G. Latterner
by the
following members
of the
Training Branch
of
Federal Electric Corp.:
Richard D. Colvin
David M. Dresdner
Charles M. Hathorn
Henry Shleuder
John A. Spiech
Gerald M. Uslan
Barry L. Warner
Walter L. Wilk*

FEDERAL ELECTRIC CORPORATION

A Subsidiary of International Telephone & Telegraph Corp.

TRANSISTORS

A Self-Instructional Programed Manual

*Under the
Editorship of
Dr. Irving L. Kosow*

Prentice-Hall, Inc. Englewood Cliffs, New Jersey

Current printing (last digit):

16   15   14   13   12

PRENTICE-HALL INTERNATIONAL, INC., LONDON
PRENTICE-HALL OF AUSTRALIA, PTY., LTD., SYDNEY
PRENTICE-HALL OF CANADA, LTD., TORONTO
PRENTICE-HALL OF INDIA (PRIVATE) LTD., NEW DELHI
PRENTICE-HALL OF JAPAN, INC., TOKYO
PRENTICE-HALL DE MEXICO, S.A., MEXICO CITY

TO THE STUDENT

You are about to participate in a new learning technique which is probably unlike anything you have previously experienced.

In the classical classroom atmosphere, a teacher generally imparts knowledge to a group of students by using a combination of lectures, demonstrations, verbal and written examinations, and, if possible, student participation through discussion.

The classical teaching method has certain built-in drawbacks. Generally a student listens; takes notes (some of which turn out to be undecipherable); studies textbook assignments (parts of which he may not fully understand); and takes examinations. At the end of a stipulated period of time the student receives a grade that is supposed to indicate his mastery of the material he has studied. But does it, really? Perhaps the student was lucky — he happened to cram just the right subject matter. However, more often than not, the student is unlucky; he was absent from class when an important subject was covered; or, on another occasion, he slumbered on, lulled into a trance by the monotonous lecturer; or, he was bored because the instructor had to go slowly in order that the less talented student could keep up with him.

Wouldn't it be nice if we could eliminate all the stumbling blocks in the classical teaching approach? Just imagine what it would be like if we could eliminate the dull lecturer; have texts that were crystal clear; know exactly how we are doing at all times; and most important, have the chance to actively participate at all time at our own rate of speed, not held back by other slower students, or not forced to go faster than we are able! What a pleasure it would be!

There is one way of doing this: We could hire an instructor as a personal tutor, and he could fulfill our specific needs. But this is hardly practical in most instances. Another way must be found.

v

That way has been found! It is called *programed instruction*, and it is an unusual, dramatic approach to learning.

The course that you will begin shortly is very *unusual* because there is *no instructor, no textbook* for homework or exams, and *no regular classroom* period.

How can such a peculiar course teach? The psychologists say that *programed instruction* can teach because the student is always participating – that he knows immediately whether he is right or wrong – and that he can go at any speed he pleases, any time he pleases. This is how the pyschologists look at a student. This probably resembles the psychologist's view of any other animal in his laboratory! From the student's point of view, programed instruction can teach because it is enjoyable, easy, painless, and *fast*. As much as one-half the time of regular classroom work is eliminated by use of this new method.

So much for the advantages of programed instruction. You are interested in how it operates.

How the Course Is Constructed

In order that you complete this course with maximum benefit, it is necessary to understand its construction. Division of the material into "parts" is necessary for convenient presentation. A part is one major topic of study.

Each part is broken down into "sets." A set is the minimum recommended amount of work for one learning period because it contains one major idea or circuit description. The average time required to complete a set is thirty minutes and none should take longer than one hour.

Each set is composed of "frames," which are minute bits of information. The completion of a "frame" should not take you more than a minute. The frames are the working parts of the course. Once you understand how to complete a frame, the program will go smoothly. In summary, the course is divided into the following:

Part	one major subject
Set	one major idea
Frame	working parts

Occasionally a Frame or Set will require additional information. The diagrams and "Panels" of written data you will need are included on the same page as the frame referring to them.

Hints

for

Successfully

Completing

the

Program

When you finish this section, you will be told to use the text. You will find that in almost every frame you will be asked to give an answer or fill in a word or two on a blank line. The correct response will be given to you immediately so you can check yourself.

If you should happen to get a wrong answer or cannot answer the question in a reasonable time (one minute or so), don't worry about it. Everyone occasionally will give a wrong answer. An incorrect response could indicate that you read too quickly and should re-read the frame. One, or even several wrong answers per set will not hinder your learning.

The answers are usually easy to fill in — in fact, you may think the frame is so simple that it is a trick question. But there are no intentional tricks in this course. Some frames will take slightly longer than others, but all are easy.

There's nothing wrong with going back over a Set if you feel you missed an important point – but since it is not the objective of this course to teach you *everything* in *every* set, repeating it will not greatly benefit you. It *is* the goal of every set to help you understand an idea or to reach a conclusion of your own.

Even a programed text can become boring if you work without taking a break. We suggest that you always rest at the logical place, the end of a set. Of course, you should finish a set before ending your study period.

When you turn to the first page of this program you will find a group of short paragraphs or frames. Place a thick sheet of paper or cardboard over the page.

To begin the program, slide the thick paper down to the words "Sample Questions." Read the *instructions carefully*. Then pull down the cover sheet until you can read the title and the first frame. (The top of the cover sheet should just meet the arrow point in the left-hand margin.) When you have filled in the blank, pull the cover down to the second frame; the answer to the first frame will also be read in the left-hand margin. Continue this operation throughout the course, and you are on your way to acquiring useful knowledge about transistors.

(1) Read the first exercise carefully and put your answer in the space provided or in the space under the exercise.

(2) Pull your cover sheet down until the arrow appears in the left-hand margin.

(3) Repeat this procedure for each succeeding exercise.

(4) When you have completed the last exercise on the page, remove the cover sheet, turn the page, replace the lower sheet, and continue with the program.

(5) *Don't fret* if you get a wrong answer. THIS IS NOT A TEST.

Sample

Questions

To learn about transistors, a person must be taught. The classroom employs a teacher and group technique of teaching. This course that you are taking _____ (does, does not) employ such a technique.

⟱

does not

Programed Instruction is the technique used in this course. Since the student does not have a human teacher or use a classical classroom approach, P _____ I _____ is essentially a new teaching technique.

⟱

Programed Instruction

A new teaching technique employed in this course is called _____ and does not use the classroom or human teacher.

⟱

Programed Instruction

Programed instruction is primarily designed to:
(1) eliminate teachers and classrooms
(2) teach the student by a new technique
(3) make money for its inventor.
    (Pick one)

⟱

(2)

CONTENTS

xi

xiv

TRANSISTORS

A Self-Instructional Programed Manual

PART ONE

TRANSISTOR THEORY

set **1** **CLASSIFICATION OF MATTER**

⇩ Look around you. Everything you see can be considered *matter*. Cigarettes, water, and people are examples of _____.

matter

⇩ All matter that we see about us has one thing in common; it *occupies space*. Therefore, to be classified as matter an object or thing must at least _____.

occupy space

⇩ A pencil is classified as _____ because it occupies space.

matter

⇩ Matter is something that _____.

occupies space

⇩ Let's take a look at a vacuum. It occupies space but is not considered matter. It is not classified as matter because it does not have any *mass*. Therefore, another requirement of matter is that it must have _____.

mass

⇩ A 1000 lb object has more _____ than a 100 lb object.

mass

⌁ If an object does not have any _____, it
cannot be classified as matter.

mass

To be classified as matter, an object must:
(1) _____.
⌁ (2) Have _____.

Occupy space
mass

One form of matter is different from another form
of matter because its elements are different. Matter
⌁ is composed of _____.

elements

The characteristics of matter are determined by the
⌁ _____ that comprise the matter.

elements

At present, there are 102 different known elements.
Examples of some of these are: oxygen, nickel, cop-
per, mercury, uranium, etc. Each of these elements
is a different kind of matter. Since all matter must
occupy space and have mass, each element must also
⌁ _____ and have _____.

occupy space
mass

Elements are particular kinds of matter; they can
neither be chemically created nor chemically broken
down. Particular kinds of matter called _____
can neither be chemically created nor chemically
⌁ broken down.

elements

4

There are 102 basic kinds of matter called elements. Elements _____ (can, cannot) be chemically broken down and _____ (can, cannot) be chemically created.

cannot
cannot

_____ are particular kinds of matter because they cannot be chemically created or chemically broken down.

Elements

The 102 basic kinds of matter can neither be chemically _____ or chemically _____.

created
broken down

When two or more elements are chemically combined, the resulting matter is called a *compound*. Table salt is a chemical combination of sodium and chlorine. Table salt is a _____.

compound

The elements in a _____ are chemically combined.

compound

To form a compound from two distinct elements we must _____ combine them.

chemically

Water is a _____ because it is a chemical combination of hydrogen and oxygen.

compound

5

Calcium carbonate is a chemical combination of calcium, carbon, and oxygen. Calcium carbonate is a
⬦ _____.

compound

It stands to reason that if we must chemically combine elements to form compounds, we must *chemically break down* a compound to isolate its elements. To retrieve sodium from salt, we must chemically
⬦ _____ the salt (compound).

break down

Compounds must be _____ broken down to
⬦ retrieve the elements that comprise it.

chemically

Compounds _____ (can, cannot) be chemi-
⬦ cally broken down.

can

(1) What are the properties of matter?
⬦ (2) What is a compound?

(1) occupies space and has mass
(2) a chemical combination of two or more elements

Since an element is a basic substance, it cannot be chemically broken down. Germanium cannot be chemically broken down. Germanium is a(n)
⬦ _____.

element

6

A compound _____ (can, cannot) be chemically broken down. An element _____ (can, cannot) be chemically broken down.

can
cannot

Hydrogen is a gas and is flammable. Oxygen is a gas which we breathe. When we chemically combine oxygen and hydrogen we produce a compound called water. The characteristics of water are _____ _____ (different from, the same as) the elements that compose it.

different from

When iron is chemically combined with oxygen to form the compound iron oxide or rust, the rust has characteristics (different from, the same as) _____ both iron and oxygen.

different from

Matter which contains more than one element not chemically combined is called a *mixture*. A tossed salad of tomatoes and lettuce is an example of a(n) _____.

mixture

The elements in a _____ are not chemically combined.

mixture

Concrete is a _____ of water, cement, sand, and gravel.

mixture

7

The elements in a _____ are not chemically combined. The elements in a _____ are chemically combined.

mixture
compound

If you mixed sand and sugar together you would produce a mixture because the substances are not chemically _____.

combined

The ingredients that comprise a mixture retain their characteristics. Oil and water is a mixture of two ingredients. The ingredients of oil and water _____ (retain, lose) their original characteristics.

retain

What are the following substances (compound, element, or mixture)?
Gold (cannot be chemically broken down).
_____ Mud (sand and water). _____
Nitric acid (chemical combination of nitrogen, hydrogen, and oxygen). _____

element
mixture
compound

Mud, gold, and nitric acid are all forms of _____ (compounds, mixtures, matter, chemical combinations).

matter

Elements cannot be _____.

chemically broken down

8

What are the three classifications of matter we have
discussed?
(1) ——————— (2) ———————.
⇨ (3) ———————. .

elements
compounds
mixtures

set **2**   **ATOMIC STRUCTURE**

The smallest particle that retains the characteristics of an element is called an *atom*. A silicon _____ is the smallest particle of the element silicon that retains its characteristics.

⇩

atom

Germanium is an element, so the smallest germanium particle is a germanium _____. Would you expect a single germanium atom to behave chemically like a one pound germanium block? _____

⇩

atom
Yes. Germanium is germanium no matter what the quantity.

Any particle that is a chemical combination of two or more atoms is a *molecule*. A water _____ contains two hydrogen atoms in chemical combination with one oxygen atom.

⇩

molecule

⇩ An oxygen atom can chemically combine with another oxygen atom to form O_2. O_2 is a m_____ .

molecule

Any substance formed by a chemical combination has more than one atom in its smallest particle. These smallest particles exhibit the characteristics of the compound and are _____ s.

⇩

molecules

10

Any substance formed by a chemical combination, the smallest particle of which contains _____ (one, more than one) atom(s) is a molecule.

⬂

more than one

Since a compound is a chemical combination of two or more elements, the smallest particle of a compound is a molecule containing _____ (less than two, two or more) atoms of different elements.

⬂

two or more

The smallest particle of a compound is a molecule. Since any compound is composed of two or more different elements, the molecule of that compound contains two or more _____ (of the same type, different type) atoms.

⬂

different type

The smallest particle of table salt (chemical combination of sodium and chlorine) is a(n) _____.
The smallest particle of H_2 (chemical combination of two atoms of the same element) is a(n) _____.

⬂

molecule
molecule

The smallest particle of carbon (a single element, not chemically combined) is a(n) _____.

⬂

atom

Complete:
A(n) _____ is the smallest particle of and exhibits the properties of a *compound.*
A(n) _____ is the smallest particle of and exhibits the properties of an element.

⬂

molecule
atom

11

All germanium atoms have the same chemical properties. What can you predict about the chemical behavior of one water molecule as compared to other water molecules?

⬩

It will behave like any other water molecule, because it has the same physical and chemical properties.

A particular kind of matter that can be broken down into one atom and still behave as the original matter is a(n) _____.

⬩

element

Atoms are the smallest particles of elements that retain the element's characteristics. Since there are 102 known elements, there are _____ chemically different atoms.

⬩

102

The element hydrogen, a gas, is different from the element carbon, a solid. An *atom* of hydrogen is _____ (different, not different) from an *atom* of carbon.

⬩

different

Atoms of the 102 elements are not the same because they contain different numbers of very minute bits of matter called *sub*-atomic particles. These sub-atomic bits are _____ (larger, smaller) than atoms.

⬩

smaller

12

An atom is composed of a heavy central body about which lighter particles revolve. Lighter particles _____ around the heavy central body of the atom.

▽

revolve

_____ (Lighter, Heavier) bodies revolve around a _____ (lighter, heavier) central body of the atom.

▽

Lighter
heavier

The heavy central body is called the *nucleus*. Light particles revolve around the _____ of an atom.

▽

nucleus

There is _____ (one, more than one) nucleus in an atom, which is _____ (heavier, lighter) than the particles orbiting around it.

▽

one
heavier

The particles revolving around the nucleus are *electrons*. _____ revolve about the nucleus.

▽

Electrons

An atom is composed of a _____ about which _____ revolve.

▽

nucleus
electrons

13

Since the nucleus is heavier than the orbiting electrons, most of the mass in an atom is located in the

▽ _____ .

nucleus

Electric charges are associated with the particles in an atom.

Electrons are negative.   Electrons are ($-$).

▽ The nucleus is positive.   The nucleus is (?).

$+$

_____ (Negative, Positive) charged electrons

▽ orbit around the positive nucleus.

Negative

Put the correct charge sign next to the sub-atomic particles.

(1) Electrons _____ .

▽ (2) Nucleus _____ .

(1) −
(2) +

For each electron there is a positive charge on the nucleus. If an atom contains 5 electrons, the nucleus

▽ contains _____ (how many?) positive charges.

5

A germanium atom has 32 electrons revolving around the nucleus. *Each* electron has _____ (how many?) negative charge(s). The nucleus of a germanium atom has _____ (how many?) posi-

▽ tive charge(s).

1

32

14

An atom of silicon has 14 _____ with one
_____ (+, −) charge each and a
_____ with 14 _____ (+, −)
charges.

⟐

electrons
(−)
nucleus
(+)

What is the relationship between the number of electrons in an atom and the number of positive charges
in the nucleus of the same atom?

They are equal; number
of electrons = number of
(+) charges.

Since in a complete atom the total number of negative charges (electrons) is equal to the total number
of positive charges, what is the total charge on the
atom?

Zero. Looking at the atom
from outside, the charges
appear to cancel out.

The number of positive charges on the nucleus is
referred to as the *atomic number*. Since the nucleus
of an arsenic atom has 33 positive charges, the
a _____ n _____ of arsenic is 33.

atomic number

The _____ of germanium is 32 because the
nucleus of a germanium atom has 32 positive charges.

atomic number

The atomic number indicates the number of
_____ charges on the _____ of an
⇔ atom.

positive
nucleus

The nuclear charge of an atom is equal to the number
of electrons, so the atomic number represents the
number of _____ as well as the nuclear
⇔ charge.

electrons

The _____ represents:
(1) Number of charges on nucleus.
⇔ (2) Number of electrons in the atom.

atomic number

The atomic number of uranium is 92.
(1) What is the positive nuclear charge?
_____

(2) How many electrons are in a uranium atom?
⇔ _____

92
92

The atomic number of an atom represents:
(1) The total charge on the _____.
⇔ (2) The number of _____.

nucleus
electrons

ELECTRON CONFIGURATION

An element having an atomic number of 21 has 21

▽ _____.

electrons

The electrons that orbit around an atomic nucleus do not travel in a random way. Each electron travels in a specific shell. If an atom has atomic number 41, there are _____ (how many?) electrons traveling around the nucleus in specific

▽ _____s.

41
shells

The orbiting electrons are confined to specific

▽ _____.

shells

The number of shells vary, depending on the number of electrons in a particular atom. In general, a large number of electrons means a large number of

▽ _____.

shells

An atom would be hopelessly complex if each electron had a different shell. Fortunately, several electrons occupy the same shell. This means that there are a _____ (smaller, greater) number of

▽ shells than electrons.

smaller

If an atom has two or more electrons, two of the electrons will be contained in the same shell. For example, if an atom has atomic number 2, both of its ▽ electrons will occupy the same _____.

shell

If an atom has two electrons, they both travel in the same shell. This shell is called the *first shell*. An atom of the element helium has two electrons. Will the ▽ electrons travel in the same shell or different shells?

The same shell — the first shell will contain two and only two electrons.

The first _____ of electrons contains ▽ _____ (how many?) electrons.

shell
two

An atom of the element hydrogen has only one elec-tron. How many electron shells are necessary in a ▽ hydrogen atom? _____

one

The physical configuration of atoms is very sys-tematic. Each shell will hold only a certain number of electrons. The first shell contains a maximum of ▽ _____ electrons.

two

The electrons in the second shell of an atom are no different from those in the first shell; they just have higher energy. You would expect the electrons in the third shell to have _____ (higher, lower) ▽ energy than those in the second shell.

higher

18

A shell is considered *filled* if it contains the required number of electrons to complete it. Except for the first shell, which contains a maximum of 2 electrons, any shell must contain 8 electrons to be considered

▽

filled

_____ .

When the second electron shell is occupied by 8 electrons, that shell is said to be _____ .

▽

filled (full, complete)

Except for the first shell of electrons, any shell is considered filled if it contains _____ electrons. The third electron shell is filled if it contains

▽

_____ electrons.

8
8

A helium atom has only 2 electrons. Only 2 electrons can occupy the *first* electron shell of an atom. The first shell of a helium atom is _____ .

▽

filled

If an atom has more than 2 electrons, the first shell will be filled. To accommodate the remaining electrons, additional _____ s must be formed.

▽

shells

A shell must be filled before another can form. The first shell of an atom requires only 2 electrons to be filled. Would the first shell be filled for an atom containing 10 electrons? _____

▽

Yes. Other shells have to be formed to accommodate the additional 8 electrons, however, the first shell must be filled so that the other shells can form.

19

The second shell of an atom can accommodate eight electrons. If a given atom has ten electrons, the first and _____ shells will be completely filled.

second

A given atom has seven electrons. The first shell of this atom contains _____ electrons. The second shell of this atom contains _____ electrons.

two
five

Panel 1

Shell	Maximum number of electrons in shell
1	2
2	8
3	18
4	32
5	32
6	18
7	8

Refer Panel 1. This is a list of the maximum number of electrons that each atomic shell can contain. The maximum number of electrons that a shell can contain is sometimes _____ (more, less) than the number required to fill a shell, which is eight electrons for all except the first shell.

more

The maximum number of electrons contained in the third shell is _____.

18

Although the maximum number of electrons in the third, fourth, fifth, and sixth shells is more than eight, these shells are considered filled when they contain _____ electrons.

eight

The electrons of an atom travel around the nucleus in _____ (paths, shells, pulses). An electron in the fourth shell differs from one in the first shell only because its energy level is _____

☟ (higher, lower).

shells
higher

Each shell has a(n) _____ (specified, unspecified), maximum number of electrons. Every shell except the _____ requires _____

☟ electrons to be filled.

specified
first
8

Complete this table. Refer to Panel 1.

Shell	Electrons required to fill shell	Maximum number in shell
1	_____	_____
2	_____	_____
3	_____	_____
4	_____	_____
5	_____	_____
6	_____	_____
7	_____	_____

☟

1 – 2 2
2 – 8 8
3 – 8 18
4 – 8 32
5 – 8 32
6 – 8 18
7 – 8 8

21

set 4

CHEMICAL BEHAVIOR OF ATOMS

An atom is considered *stable* (will not chemically react) if its outer shell is filled. A helium atom has only two electrons. Therefore, it has only one shell which is filled. The helium atom is a _____ atom.

stable

An atom is stable if its outer electron shell is _____ (empty, partially filled, filled).

filled

A stable atom must have _____ (how many?) electrons in its outer shell (except helium, atomic number 2). A stable atom _____ (will, will not) chemically react.

8

will not

Since there is a maximum of 7 electron shells, there are only 7 different atoms that can have complete outer shells. There are only _____ stable atoms.

7. The first, helium has 2 electrons in its outer shell. All the other stable atoms would have 8 electrons in the outer shell.

There are only 7 naturally stable atoms; how would you expect the remainder of the atoms to be classified? _____

Not stable or unstable

22

Anything unstable has the tendency to become stable. The same is true for atoms. An unstable atom will tend to _____ (remain unstable, become stable).

☟

become stable

The atom of the element radon has 8 electrons in its outer shell. The atom is _____. The atom of the element chlorine has 7 electrons in its outer shell. The atom is _____.

☟

stable
unstable

An unstable atom has a partially filled outer shell. A stable atom has a filled outer shell. To become stable, an unstable atom must acquire a _____ outer shell of electrons.

☟

filled (complete)

A chlorine atom has 7 electrons in its outer shell. Since a chlorine atom has a tendency to become stable, it will try to acquire _____ additional electron(s).

☟

1

A sodium atom has one electron in its outer shell. To become stable it must have a complete outer shell. Would you think it easier to acquire the seven necessary additional electrons, or give up one, leaving a complete outer shell?

☟

It is easier to give up one, because it takes less energy.

23

When an atom has an almost complete outer shell, it can become stable more easily by _____ (giving up, acquiring) electrons. When an atom has an almost empty outer shell, it can become stable by

▽ _____ (giving up, acquiring) electrons.

acquiring
giving up

An oxygen atom has 6 electrons in its outer shell. It must _____ (give up, acquire) _____

▽ (how many?) electrons to become stable.

acquire
two

A magnesium atom has 2 electrons in its outer shell. It must _____ (give up, acquire) _____ (how many?) electrons to become

▽ stable.

give up
two

An atom can become stable by _____ additional electrons or giving up electrons, depending on

▽ the number of electrons in the outer shell.

acquiring (getting)

There are two ways an unstable atom can become stable (achieve a complete outer shell):
(1) _____ electrons.

▽ (2) _____ electrons.

Acquire
Give up

24

How does an unstable atom acquire the necessary electrons to make it stable? By finding an atom (or atoms) that wants to give up the same necessary number. In the same way, an atom gives up electrons to become stable by finding an atom that needs to

⏣ _____ (give up, acquire) the same number.

acquire

A sodium atom has one electron in its outer shell. A chlorine atom has 7 electrons in its outer shell. The sodium atom will _____ one electron to the

⏣ chlorine atom. Then both atoms are stable.

give (give up) (transfer)

When the sodium atom gives an electron to the chlorine atom, this event is called a *chemical reaction*. If a chlorine atom acquires an electron from a sodium

⏣ atom, a _____ takes place.

chemical reaction

If a hydrogen atom gives up an electron to a chlorine atom, a(n) _____ (chemical reaction, atomic displacement, nuclear explosion) takes place. When a chemical reaction occurs, a chemical com-

⏣ bination (technical term: compound) is the result.

chemical reaction

If chemicals react (acquiring and giving up elec-trons) a chemical combination of elements, called a

⏣ _____, is produced.

compound

A helium atom has an atomic number of 2, so it has
_____ electrons. Is it a stable atom (outer
⇨ shell filled)? _____

2

Yes. First shell only needs
two to be complete.

An aluminum atom has 3 electrons in its outer shell.
Is the aluminum atom stable? _____ If it is
unstable, how many electrons must the aluminum
⇨ atom give up? _____

No

3

For an atom with 6 electrons in its outer shell, it is
_____ (easier, more difficult) to acquire
⇨ two electrons than to give away 6 electrons.

easier

A calcium atom has 2 electrons in its outer shell. A
sulfur atom has 6 electrons in its outer shell. Would
you expect a sulfur atom and a calcium atom to react
⇨ chemically? _____

Yes. The calcium atom
would give away 2 elec-
trons to the sulfur atom,
forming a calcium-sulfur
compound.

PERIODIC TABLE

Unfold the periodic table located at the back of the book and refer to it as needed throughout this set.

Many *similarities* exist among the elements. Often the physical properties of different elements are

▽   s _____ .

similar

Both sodium and potassium are soft metals having a metallic luster and both react readily with other elements. The physical properties of sodium and

▽   potassium are s _____ .

similar

Physical similarities appear in elements because of similar (*not* identical) atomic structures of the elements. The atomic properties of two elements are said to be _____ if they contain the same num-

▽   ber of electrons in their outer shell.

similar

If the physical and atomic properties of two elements are similar, you would expect the two elements to have _____ (the same, a different) number

▽   of electrons in their outer shells.

the same

An element has both physical and atomic properties. Hardness is a(n) _____ (physical, atomic) property. Number of electrons in an outer shell is a(n) _____ property.

physical
atomic

The elements can be arranged into charts or tables according to their properties. One such arrangement is called the *periodic* table. The atomic number of oxygen could be obtained by consulting a periodic _____.

table

The _____ table is an arrangement of the elements according to their atomic properties.

periodic

A most important tabular arrangement of the elements according to their atomic properties is the _____.

periodic table

Since the atomic properties of an element determine its physical properties, the periodic table can reveal an element's physical as well as its atomic _____.

properties (structure)

The _____ properties of an element determine the _____ properties, and can be discovered by referring to the _____ _____.

atomic
physical
periodic table

28

Atomic and physical _____ of the 102 elements, are systematically arranged in the periodic table.

properties

The _____ are represented in the periodic table by their symbols and their atomic numbers.

⇩

elements

The 102 known elements are arranged in the form of a periodic table. You would expect the numbers on the periodic table to go from 1 to _____.

⇩

102

Since the number of electrons in an atom is equal to the nuclear charge, the atomic number of an element is equal to the number of electrons contained in its atom. The atomic number of silicon (Si) is 14. Therefore, its atom contains _____ electron(s).

⇩

14

Referring to the periodic table, sodium (Na) has _____ electron(s). (It will be in group I, Period 3.)

⇩

11

The electrons in the outer shell of an atom are valence electrons. Sodium (Na) has one electron in its outer ring. Therefore it has one _____ electron.

⇩

valence

A germanium atom has atomic number 32; it has four electrons in its outer shell. A germanium atom has a total of _____ electrons, and _____ (how many?) valence electrons.

⇩

32

4

29

In the periodic table, all the elements appearing in the same vertical column have the same number of valence electrons. Magnesium (Mg) and calcium (Ca) appear in the same vertical column. Therefore, they both have the same number of ＿＿＿＿＿＿＿ electrons.

valence

A vertical column is called a *group*. In the periodic table all the elements appearing in a g＿＿＿＿＿ have the same number of ＿＿＿＿＿＿ electrons.

group
valence

In the periodic table Mg and Ca appear in the same ＿＿＿＿＿＿＿ because they have the same number of valence electrons.

group

A group in the periodic table is a ＿＿＿＿＿＿ (horizontal, vertical) column.

vertical

The number of valence electrons in an atom corresponds to the group in which that element appears. Calcium (Ca) appears in group II; Ca has ＿＿＿＿＿＿＿ valence electron(s).

2

Referring to the periodic table, silicon (Si) has ＿＿＿＿＿＿＿ valence electron(s).

4

Na and K appear in the same _____. These elements have common properties in that both are soft metals having a metallic luster and both react readily with other elements.

⇩

group

Referring again to the periodic table, Na and K also have _____ (how many?) valence electron(s) since both appear in group _____.

⇩

1

I

Silicon (Si) and germanium (Ge) both appear in group _____ (Roman numeral). These elements have common physical and chemical properties because they both have _____ (how many?) valence electrons.

⇩

IV

4

Elements appearing in the same _____ have atoms containing _____ (the same, a different) number of electrons in the outer shell.

⇩

group

the same

In the periodic table a horizontal row is called a *period*. All the elements appearing in the same horizontal row appear in the same p_____.

⇩

period

Elements occurring in the same horizontal row or _____ have a different relationship from elements occurring in the same vertical column or _____.

⇩

period

group

31

The atoms of all elements occurring in the same period have the same number of *electron shells*. Lithium (Li) and carbon (C) both have two

⇩ _____.

electron shells

Silicon (Si) and chlorine (Cl) both occur in the same _____; they both have the same number of

⇩ electron shells.

period

The number of electron shells in an atom corresponds to the period in which that element occurs. Calcium (Ca) occurs in period 4, thus Ca has _____

⇩ electron shells.

4

Referring to the periodic table, the element Si has _____ (how many?) electron shells because

⇩ it is in period _____.

3
3

Germanium (Ge), gallium (Ga), and arsenic (As) all occur in period _____. These elements

⇩ all have _____ electron shells.

4 (*or* 4B)
4

The *period* number indicates the number of _____ in a particular atom. The *group* number indicates the number of _____ in the

⇩ outer shell of a particular atom.

electron shells
electrons
(valence electrons)

32

The electrons in the outer shell of an atom are

⇩ _____ electrons.

valence

Silicon appears in group IV, period 3. This means
that a silicon atom has _____ valence elec-

⇩ trons and _____ electron shells.

4
3

The element strontium appears in group II, period 5;
this means that a strontium atom has 2 _____

⇩ _____ s and 5 _____ s.

valence electrons
electron shells (not outer
shells)

Silver atoms have one valence electron and 5 electron
shells. Silver appears in group _____, period

⇩ _____.

I
5

CHEMICAL BONDS IN METALS AND CRYSTALS

A chemical compound is formed when the atom of one element gives up its valence electron to the atom of another element. Both atoms will then be

▽ _____ (stable, unstable, polystable).

stable

The *valence* electrons of an atom are in the _____ (inner, outer, empty) shell and are the electrons which determine the chemical properties of the atom. If an atom gives up electrons, they will

▽ be valence electrons.

outer

A chemical compound is formed by one atom which gives up _____ and one atom which acquires those _____. This chemical com-

▽ pound is called an *ionic* compound.

electrons
electrons

The stable atoms resulting from the giving up and acquiring of electrons are called *ions,* so the chemical compound is logically a(n)_____ic com-

▽ pound.

ionic

An ionic compound consists of stable atoms called

▽ _____s.

ions

A single uncombined atom has a net charge of zero because the positive nuclear charge is equal to the ⇩ number of negatively charged _____.

electrons

If a single atom becomes stable by chemically combining with another (losing or acquiring electrons), the net charge of the atom will _____ (change, remain unchanged) because electron loss ⇩ or gain will alter the total negative charge.

change

Assume that a fluorine atom (which combining with another atom) acquires one electron and becomes stable. Since the additional electron has a negative charge, the net charge of the stable fluorine ion is ⇩ _____ (+1, 0, −1).

−1

Assume that a sodium atom (atomic number 11) gives up one electron to become stable. Since the lost electron has a negative charge, the net charge of the ⇩ stable sodium ion is _____ (+1, 0, −1).

+1

When an unstable atom becomes stable by giving up or acquiring electrons, its net charge will _____ (change, not change) depending on ⇩ the number of electrons transferred.

change

⇩ When an atom gives up or acquires electrons, the resulting charged particle is a(n) _____.

ion

Ions _____ (are, are not) electrically charged, because they acquire or give up electrons.

are

Single uncombined atoms _____ (do, do not) have a net electrical charge because the number of electrons is equal to the number of nuclear charges.

do not

An atom of sodium gives up the one electron in its outer shell to an atom of chlorine, completing the chlorine atom outer shell. A sodium ion with a charge of _____ (+1, −1, 0) has been formed and a chlorine _____ with a charge of _____ (+1, −1, 0) has been formed.

+1
ion
−1

An ionic compound is formed when an unstable atom gives up to or acquires electrons from another atom forming stable atoms or _____ s.

ions

In an ionic compound, the ion formed by an atom giving up electrons is _____ (+, −) charged; the ion formed by an atom acquiring electrons is _____ (+, −) charged.

+
−

A positively charged particle will be attracted to a negatively charged particle. A positively charged ion will be attracted to a _____ ion.

negatively charged

36

The ions in a ionic compound stay close together because one ion is _____ charged and the
⇩ other ion is _____ charged.

positively
negatively
(either order)

An ionic compound is composed of _____ (ions, unstable atoms, electrons) which remain together because of their _____ (identical,
⇩ opposite) charge.

ions
opposite

Atom number 1 gives up the 2 electrons in its outer shell to atom number 2 with 6 electrons in its outer shell. The result is the formation of _____ (how many?) ions. Atom number 1 becomes an ion with a charge of _____ (+2, 0, −2). Atom number 2 becomes an ion with a charge of
⇩ _____ (+2, 0, −2).

2
+2
−2

The ions in an ionic compound have _____ (opposite, the same) charge(s). Therefore, the ions are attracted to each other. In an ionic compound, we call the force of attraction an ionic *bond*. The force of _____ (attraction, repulsion) be-
⇩ tween ions constitutes an ionic _____.

opposite
attraction
bond

The oppositely charged ions of an ionic compound remain together because of a force of attraction called
⇩ an ionic _____.

bond

37

Select the key phrase that best describes an ionic bond.
(1) Attraction between electrons.
(2) Unstable atoms.
✧ (3) Force of attraction between ions.

(3) Force of attraction between ions

A chemical compound is ionically bonded if:
(1) it contains oppositely charged stable atoms, called _____ s and
✧ (2) these remain together because of their force of _____ for each other.

ions
attraction

Ionic bonds occur in some chemical compounds, but the structures of other substances must be explained by other bonds. A metallic element, for example, has the same kind of atoms throughout, so there _____ (will, will not) be oppositely charged ✧ ions.

will not

The periodic table indicates that all metals have either 1, 2, or 3 valence electrons. A carbon atom has 4 valence electrons and _____ (is, is not) a ✧ metal.

is not

A sodium (metal) atom has one valence electron. Can that sodium atom become stable by accepting an electron from another sodium atom? Why or why not? (Explain by using the number of electrons in outer shell required for stability.)

No. The sodium atom would then have two valence electrons. To be stable, it must have eight electrons in the outer shell.

Assume that a large group of iron atoms is congregated; since there are no other atoms around to acquire the valence electrons, these electrons travel about in a random motion inside the metal. These random electrons form an *electron cloud* around the metal atoms. Since the electron cloud contains only electrons it must be _____ (positive, negative).

negative

Since each metallic atom contributes its valence electrons (negatively charged) to the electron cloud, the remaining stable atoms assume a net _____ (positive, negative) charge.

positive

The electron cloud, being negatively charged, surrounds the positively charged atoms. Since the positively charged atoms are attracted to the negative cloud, the metallic atoms are bound to each other. The *electron* _____ acts as a glue.

cloud

In an ionic bond, each positive ion was attracted by a negative ion, and there was no electron cloud. In a _____ (electronic, metallic, ceramic) bond, the positively charged atoms are held together by an electron cloud.

metallic

In an ionic bond, there are no free electrons; each electron has its particular place in the outer shell of the atoms. Is this the case in a metallic bond?

No. The electrons are free and do not belong to any particular atom.

For transistor materials, a bond different from ionic and metallic bonds is incorporated for the combination of atoms; it is the *covalent* b_____.

⬦

bond

To become stable, an atom must have a complete outer shell. When an atom has 4 valence electrons, it requires _____ (how many?) additional electrons to become stable.

⬦

4

A covalent bond is formed between atoms which share valence electrons. For a germanium atom (4 valence electrons) to be stable, it must share

⬦ _____ additional electrons.

4

Consider an element that is composed of atoms which have 4 valence electrons. A co_____ bond between atoms would exist if the atoms shared electrons to reach stability.

⬦

covalent

If two squirrels *co*-habit a dwelling, they *share* that dwelling. If two people *co*operate, it means they *share* in an operation. In a covalent bond, you would

⬦ expect atoms to _____ their valence electrons.

share

The configuration which atoms assume while sharing electrons determines the crystal structure of the element. This sharing of electrons is called a

⬦ _____ bond.

covalent

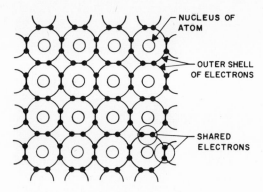

NUCLEUS OF ATOM

OUTER SHELL OF ELECTRONS

SHARED ELECTRONS

TYPICAL COVALENT BOND

Figure 1

In a covalent bond the atoms _____ electrons. Figure 1 indicates a typical covalent bond.

share

Atoms in a germanium crystal (each having four valence electrons) have a stable configuration because they _____ electrons. A germanium crystal is the result of _____ bonding.

share
covalent

In covalent bonds, each electron must be shared between a particular pair of atoms. Is this different from the metallic bond? _____

Yes. The metallic bond has free electrons.

Match the type of bond to the most descriptive phrase.
(1) ionic bond   (a) has an electron cloud
(2) metallic bond   (b) electrons are shared
(3) covalent bond   (c) atoms acquire
                            electrons

(1)–(c)
(2)–(a)
(3)–(b)

41

In covalent bonded atoms, all the valence electrons of an atom are shared with other atoms. This means that in a crystal formed by covalent bonds, there _____ (will, will not) be free electrons.

will not

An ionic compound is formed when atoms acquire and give up electrons to form a stable configuration. An ionic compound _____ (will, will not) have free electrons, because all the atoms form ions.

will not

In metals, an electron cloud is formed by the valence electrons of the metal atoms but the electrons do not belong to particular atoms. Metallic bonded substances _____ (will, will not) contain free electrons.

will

A _____ bond is distinguished by an electron cloud and it provides free _____ s.

metallic
electrons

A covalent bond is distinguished by the absence of free _____ s and is formed when the atoms of the compound _____ electrons.

electrons
share

set 7

CONDUCTION, INSULATION, AND PARTIAL CONDUCTION OF CRYSTALS

In electronics, a fundamental property of any crystal is its ability or inability to conduct electricity. The knowledge that a crystal will conduct _____ (is, is not) important.

is

According to its degree of conductivity, a crystal is classified as a conductor, a non-_____, or a *partial* _____.

conductor
conductor

Name three classifications of crystals according to their conductive properties.
(1) _____.   (2) _____.
(3) _____.

conductor
non-conductor
partial conductor
(any order)

The physical and electrical properties of a crystal depend on its atomic structure. Conduction, an electrical property, depends on the _____ structure of the crystal.

atomic

Conduction is the movement of electrons. If electrons cannot move, conduction _____ (can, cannot) take place.

cannot

43

In a crystal, conduction can occur if electrons are free to move. The more free electrons that are available, the _____ (easier, harder) it will be for the crystal to conduct.

easier

Three crystals that differ in their conductive properties are metallic* crystals, covalent* crystals, and ionic* crystals. The conduction of each crystal _____ (will, will not) depend on the availability of free electrons in the crystal.

*These terms imply the bonds associated with crystal structure.

will

_____ contain free electrons in their electron cloud. In covalent compounds, electrons are _____ d between atoms. In _____ compounds, all electrons belong exclusively to particular ions.

Metals
shared
ionic

When a crystal conducts, free electrons must be available to move. Which crystal has free electrons, a metallic crystal or an ionic crystal? _____ A _____ ic crystal will conduct.

metallic crystal
metallic

A covalent crystal is composed of atoms which share electrons; from your knowledge of conduction (movement of free electrons) would you expect a covalent crystal to conduct? _____

Since the valence electrons of a covalent crystal are shared, there are no free electrons; hence, no conduction.

44

A metallic crystal has free electrons; it _____ (will, will not) conduct. An ionic crystal has no free electrons; it _____ (will, will not) conduct. A covalent crystal has no free electrons; it _____ (will, will not) normally conduct.

will
will not
will not

Compounds formed by _____ bonds or _____ bonds will not conduct because of the absence of _____s.

covalent
ionic
(either order)
free electrons

A crystal that will not conduct is called an *insulator*. A diamond crystal has no free electrons, so it is a(n) _____.

insulator

Insulators will not conduct. Ionic and covalent bonded compounds are _____.

insulators

Classify the following crystals as conductors or insulators.
Metallic crystal: _____.
Covalent crystal: _____.
Ionic crystal: _____.

conductor
insulator
insulator

Ionic and covalent bonded materials will not conduct because they do not contain free electrons, but electrons can be freed if enough energy is available. Electrons in ionic and covalent materials can be _____ (freed, captured, created) by sufficient energy.

⇩

freed

In ionic compounds, extremely high energy is required to yank an electron away from an ion; such energy is not readily available. You would expect all ionic compounds to be classified as _____ (insulators, conductors, transistors).

⇩

insulators

Ionic compounds are classified as insulators because high _____ is required to yank away electrons and free them from the stable ionic compound.

⇩

energy

A material that requires high _____ to free electrons for conduction is an insulator. An ionic compound is a(n) _____.

⇩

energy
insulator

In covalent bonds, energy is required to free electrons from the covalent bond. If high enough energy can be supplied, _____ (what kind of?) bonds will be broken and _____s will be freed.

⇩

covalent
electrons

Assume a covalent crystal to which energy has been added so that some covalent bonds are broken.
(1) Some of the electrons shared between atoms will be set _____.
(2) These electrons will allow the crystal to _____ (conduct, insulate, destroy itself).

⮂

free
conduct

Usually covalent crystals will not _____. If _____ is supplied to a covalent crystal, it could possibly _____.

⮂

conduct
energy
conduct

Substances having metallic bonds will conduct under _____ (no, some, all) circumstances, because free electrons are _____ (always, sometimes, never) available.

⮂

all
always

Ionic compounds will conduct under _____ (all, some, almost no) circumstances because free electrons are _____ (always, sometimes, almost never) available due to high stability of the ion.

⮂

almost no
almost never

Covalent substances will conduct under _____ (all, some, no) circumstances (for instance high energy applied) because free electrons are _____ (always, sometimes, never) available.

⮂

some
sometimes

47

ENERGY DIAGRAMS — INSULATORS: CONDUCTORS, SEMICONDUCTORS

All crystals can have their conductive properties represented by simple *energy diagrams*. The conductive properties of a crystal considered to be an insulator can be described by an _____ .

✧

energy diagram

A metallic crystal can have its conductive properties
✧ represented by _____ diagrams.

energy

In an energy diagram the properties of a crystal which permit or inhibit the _____ of an electrical current through the crystal are represented
✧ by a picture.

conduction

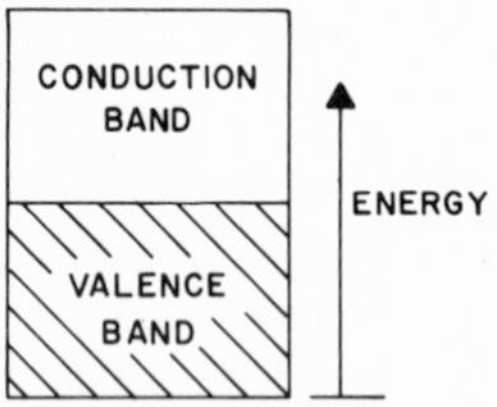

CONDUCTION BAND

ENERGY

VALENCE BAND

ENERGY DIAGRAM
FOR METAL

Figure 2

Refer to Figure 2. This is an energy diagram for a metallic crystal. The two bands are the:
✧ (1) _____ .   (2) _____ .

conduction
valence

The valence band contains the valence electrons of the metallic crystal. For a crystal to conduct, electrons must be contained in the conduction band. In a metal, valence electrons must move from the _____ band to the _____ band before the metal can conduct.

☞

valence
conduction

The valence band contains valence electrons, which are free electrons in a metal. These free electrons must be transferred to the _____ band from the _____ band for conduction to take place.

☞

conduction
valence

Look at Figure 2 again. It takes energy to move an electron from the valence band to the conduction band. In metals, the two bands are adjacent, so _____ (little, high, extremely high) energy is required for the transfer.

☞

little

_____ is required to move electrons from the valence band to the conduction band; since these bands are adjacent in a metal, the energy required is _____.

☞

Energy
small

The energy diagram of a metallic crystal has _____ (how many?) bands. _____ is required to move a(n) _____ from one band to another.

☞

2
Energy
electron

If electrons occupy the conduction band the crystal will conduct. Since metals conduct, metals have electrons in the ＿＿＿＿＿＿＿ band.

conduction

Electrons will be in the conduction band if the metal crystal has any energy at all, and it always has some heat energy to move the electrons to the conduction band. For this reason, we say that metals will ＿＿＿＿＿＿＿ (never, sometimes, always) conduct.

always

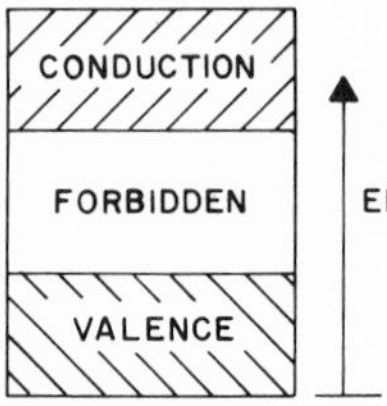

GENERAL ENERGY DIAGRAM

Figure 3

Refer to Figure 3. This is a general energy diagram for a crystal. The three bands are the:
(1) ＿＿＿＿＿＿. (2) ＿＿＿＿＿＿.
(3) ＿＿＿＿＿＿.

valence
forbidden
conduction
(any order)

Since this is a general diagram, it can be modified to represent a ＿＿＿＿＿＿＿ crystal if the forbidden band is removed.

metallic

The forbidden band represents an energy gap which an electron must cross. With an extremely high gap, you would expect a crystal to be a(n) _____ (insulator, conductor, resistor).

⇩

insulator, since conduction could only take place when electrons cross the wide forbidden band.

In a covalent crystal the forbidden band would represent the energy required to break a covalent bond and permit conduction. A narrow forbidden band would indicate a covalent bond which can be broken _____ (easily, with difficulty).

easily

A _____ (covalent, ionic, metallic) crystal has no forbidden zone in its energy diagram. A covalent crystal, if it were a good insulator would have an extremely _____ (wide, narrow, negligible) forbidden zone.

metallic
wide

For conduction to occur in a covalent crystal, electrons must jump from the _____ zone, across the _____ zone, and into the _____ zone.

valence
forbidden
conduction

The energy diagrams of insulators have wide _____ zones. A wide _____ zone indicates that _____ (high, low, intermediate) energy is required for conduction.

forbidden
forbidden
high

51

Energy diagrams of metals have no _____
zones. If a crystal has no such zone, it will always
⇩ _____ (conduct, insulate).

forbidden
conduct

What about crystals that have forbidden zones representing narrow energy gaps? If energy can be added
to make electrons jump the forbidden zone, the crys-
⇩ tal will _____.

conduct

Crystals which have narrow forbidden zones are
called *semiconductors,* because they conduct under
special conditions. A crystal which conducts because
its electrons jump a narrow forbidden zone is a
⇩ _____.

semiconductor

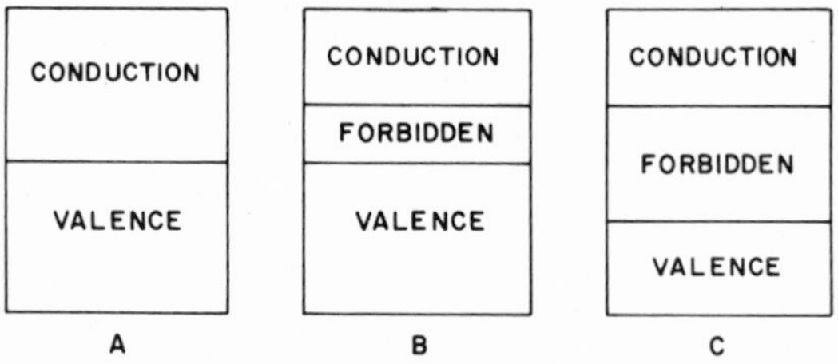

CONDUCTION		CONDUCTION		CONDUCTION
		FORBIDDEN		
VALENCE		VALENCE		FORBIDDEN
				VALENCE
A		B		C

Figure 4

Refer to Figure 4.
Figure 4a is an energy diagram for a(n)
_____.

Figure 4b is an energy diagram for a(n)
_____.

Figure 4c is an energy diagram for a(n)
⇩ _____.

metal conductor
semiconductor
non-conductor (insulator)

A semiconductor crystal has a _____ zone, but it is narrow enough for electrons to jump across it with the addition of a small amount of energy.

forbidden

A _____ is a crystal that has _____ (a wide, a narrow, no) forbidden band, across which electrons jump with a small addition of energy.

semiconductor
a narrow

Metallic crystals are joined by metallic bonds (electron cloud) and _____ (will, will not) conduct. Ionic crystals are composed of charged ions and _____ (will, will not) conduct. Covalent crystals are formed by shared electron bonds (covalent) and will _____ (always, never, sometimes) conduct.

will
will not
sometimes

Some covalent crystals will conduct under special conditions. A covalent crystal that will sometimes conduct must have a _____ (wide, narrow) forbidden zone; it is called a _____.

narrow
semiconductor

A semiconductor can only be formed from a _____ (metallic, ionic, covalent) crystal, since a(n) _____ crystal will always conduct, and a(n) _____ crystal will never conduct.

covalent
metallic
ionic

53

Covalent crystals that have narrow forbidden zones are _____ s. Covalent crystals that have wide forbidden zones are _____ s.

Metallic crystals can only be _____ s. Ionic crystals can only be _____ s. Covalent crystals can be either _____ s or _____ s. (Insert the word conductors, insulators or semiconductors.)

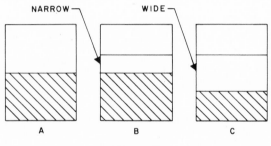

Figure 5

Refer to Figure 5. Classify each of these energy diagrams according to the conduction properties (conductor, insulator, semiconductor).

5a _____.
5b _____.
5c _____.

set 9

INTRINSIC AND EXTRINSIC SEMICONDUCTORS

Semiconductors which are made from pure substances are called *intrinsic semiconductors*. In _____ semiconductors, the energy diagram will be the same for every atom, since in a pure substance all atoms ▽ are the same.

intrinsic

Germanium, a covalent crystal, has an energy diagram with a narrow forbidden band. Pure germanium ▽ would be a(n) _____ semiconductor.

intrinsic

Pure semiconductors are called _____ semiconductors. These semiconductors, like any other, depend on the movement of _____ from the ▽ valence band to the conduction band.

intrinsic
electrons

Pure crystals which require small amounts of energy to make _____ jump from the valence band to the conduction band are called _____ ▽ semiconductors.

electrons
intrinsic

The amount of conduction in any crystal depends on the number of electrons in the conduction band. The amount of conduction in an intrinsic semiconductor (crystalline structure) would depend on the _____ (quality, quantity, Q-factor) of elec- ▽ trons in the _____ band.

quantity
conduction

55

The higher the number of electrons in the conduction band, the _____ (more, less) conduction will take place.

more

Small energy will give one electron the necessary push across the forbidden band. With high energy, the crystal would allow _____ (more, less, no) electrons to jump the gap.

more

If high energy is applied to a semiconductor crystal, (choose one)
(1) the crystal will glow.
(2) more electrons will jump the forbidden band.
(3) there will be more electrons in the valence band.

(2)—Electrons will jump from the valence band to the conduction band.

If higher energy is applied to a semiconductor crystal, _____ (more, less) electrons will appear in the conduction band. The more electrons in the conduction band, the _____ (higher, lower) the conduction of current.

more
higher

An increase in applied energy to an intrinsic semiconductor will _____ its conduction.

increase

An intrinsic semiconductor is composed of _____ (pure, impure) crystals that require _____ (energy, no energy) for conduction.

pure
energy

56

The energy diagram of an intrinsic semiconductor will have three bands:

(1) _____. (2) _____.

⟁ (3) _____.

valence
forbidden
conduction
(any order)

In an intrinsic semiconductor, conduction depends on the number of electrons in the _____ band, which got there by jumping the _____

⟁ band.

conduction
forbidden

More soap, more shine. In intrinsic semiconductors, more energy, more _____ (shine, purity,

⟁ conduction, attraction).

conduction

Decreasing the energy applied to an intrinsic semiconductor will allow the electrons in the conduction band to fall back into the valence band. To sustain the conduction in an intrinsic semiconductor, we

⟁ must sustain the _____.

energy

Intrinsic semiconductors are pure crystals; conduction in intrinsic semiconductor material depends on the application of _____ to provide free

⟁ electrons.

energy

Extrinsic semiconductors are *impure* crystals. To make an extrinsic semiconductor, we would add an impurity to a pure crystal, called an _____ semiconductor. Impurity + intrinsic crystal = _____ crystal.

↧

intrinsic
extrinsic (impure)

An _____ semiconductor is one which contains impurities.

↧

extrinsic

Because an extrinsic semiconductor was originally an intrinsic semiconductor before _____ were added, similar energy diagrams are used for both types.

↧

impurities

Extrinsic semiconductor = _____ semiconductor + _____.

↧

intrinsic
impurities

Varying the energy applied to an intrinsic semiconductor varies the number of conduction band electrons and the conduction increases or decreases. Increasing the energy applied to an *extrinsic* semiconductor will make an electron jump the forbidden band to the conduction band; conduction will _____ (increase, decrease).

↧

increase

Applied energy is fundamentally important in determining the conduction of both _____ and _____ semiconductors.

↧

intrinsic
extrinsic
(either order)

58

⎌ In extrinsic semiconductors the amount of impurity can be controlled. Would you think that the amount of impurity can also influence the conduction of a crystal? _____

It definitely will.

⎌ In extrinsic semiconductors, the amount of energy applied helps to determine the amount of conduction. The amount of impurity _____ (will, will not) affect conduction properties.

will

⎌ Conduction in intrinsic semiconductors depends on the _____ applied to the crystal. Conduction in extrinsic semiconductors depends on the _____ applied to the crystal and the amount of _____ added.

energy
energy
impurities

⎌ _____ semiconductors are made from pure crystalline material. _____ semiconductors are made from crystalline material containing impurities.

Intrinsic
Extrinsic

set **10** N-TYPE AND P-TYPE IMPURITIES

Transistors are made from semiconductor material with added impurities*, because conduction can be controlled easily with an impure crystal. Transistors are made with _____ (intrinsic, extrinsic) semiconductor material.

*These impurities will be referred to as "impurity atoms" for the sake of brevity.

⌁

extrinsic

Refer to the Periodic Table.

The elements that form intrinsic semiconductors* occur in group IV of the periodic table. This means that the atoms of the crystal have _____ (how many?) electrons in the outer shell.

*For the sake of brevity, the term "intrinsic semiconductors" will mean semiconductor material as used in the manufacture of transistors.

⌁

4

Semiconductor crystals are covalent materials, so they will share electrons. The atom of an intrinsic semiconductor, appearing in group IV of the periodic table, will have to share _____ (how many?) electrons with its neighbors to have a stable configuration.

⌁

4

Intrinsic semiconductors from group IV can be made into _____ semiconductors by adding impurities.

⌁

extrinsic

60

Assume that in an intrinsic crystal, each atom has 4 electrons, and all the electrons are shared. There are no free electrons (electrons in the conduction band) unless energy has been applied (we assume this is not the case). There are no electrons in the conduction band, so conduction _____ (will, will not) take place.

☞

will not

An intrinsic semiconductor crystal in group **IV** has atoms with _____ (how many?) electrons each in their outer shells, and all of these electrons are shared. If an atom from group **V** is inserted into this intrinsic crystal, the intrinsic crystal will _____ (remain pure, become impure).

☞

4
become impure

An atom possessing 3 or 5 electrons, when placed in an intrinsic crystal made up of atoms with 4 electrons, would be an _____ (conductor, reducer, impurity).

☞

impurity

Assume that an impurity atom with 5 electrons is placed into an intrinsic crystal. Only 4 of the electrons will be shared with intrinsic atoms. There will be one excess _____.

☞

electron

Assume that several impurity atoms with 5 valence electrons each are placed in an intrinsic crystal. How many valence electrons of each impurity atom will be shared with the intrinsic atoms? _____
How many remaining valence electrons of each impurity atom will be excess electrons? _____

☞

4
1 for each impurity atom

61

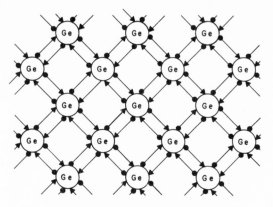

GERMANIUM CRYSTAL STRUCTURE

Figure 6

Refer to Figure 6. This is a representation of germanium crystal structure, showing the outer ring of electrons (the black dots). There are _____ (how many?) electrons in the outer shell.

🔽

4

The arrows in Figure 6 indicate the sharing of electrons in the covalent bond. Each atom shares _____ (how many?) electrons with _____ (how many?) different atoms.

🔽

4
4

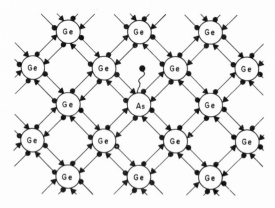

GERMANIUM CRYSTAL STRUCTURE
WITH ONE IMPURITY ATOM

Figure 7

Now refer to Figure 7. This is a representation of a germanium crystal with one impurity atom placed in the crystal structure. How many excess electrons are pictured here? _____

1

When an extrinsic semiconductor has an excess of electrons (electrons not utilized in a bond), it is an *N-type* semiconductor. When impurity atoms with five electrons are in a semiconductor, there is a(n) _____ (excess, deficiency) of electrons and the crystal is an _____ -type semiconductor.

excess
N

When an extrinsic semiconductor has a(n) _____ of electrons, it is N-type semiconductor material.

excess

Extrinsic semiconductor material having an excess of electrons is called _____ -type because excess electrons will give the crystal a Negative charge.

N

N-type semiconductor material will have _____ (a higher, the same, a lower) number of electrons than an intrinsic semiconductor.

a higher

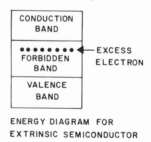

ENERGY DIAGRAM FOR
EXTRINSIC SEMICONDUCTOR

Figure 8

Figure 8, shows the energy diagram for an extrinsic semiconductor with an excess of electrons. This would be an example of _____ -type material.

N

Except for the electrons in the forbidden band, this energy diagram is similar to one for a(n) _____ .

intrinsic semiconductor or insulator

The energy diagram of an *intrinsic* semiconductor (containing no excess electrons) does not have electrons in the forbidden band. The energy diagram of an N-type *extrinsic* semiconductor (containing excess electrons) _____ (does, does not) have electrons in the forbidden band.

does

The electrons in the _____ band of an N-type energy diagram are excess electrons.

forbidden

The electrons in the forbidden band of an N-type extrinsic semiconductor are the excess electrons added by the impurity atoms. If these electrons were removed, would the crystal be: (circle one)

⟱ (1) Extrinsic   (2) Intrinsic

(1) Extrinsic, the crystal would conduct like an intrinsic crystal, but the presence of impurity atoms makes the crystal extrinsic.

The excess electrons of the impurity atoms appear on an energy diagram in the _____ band. The electrons do not fill this band, but only occupy a

⟱ certain energy level.

forbidden

In N-type material, excess electrons have a certain energy level which occurs in the forbidden band. Where do these excess electrons come from? (Circle one)

(1) the original intrinsic material

⟱ (2) the impurity atoms

(2) from the impurity atoms that made the material N-type

Notice that the excess electrons have an energy level close to the conduction band. They will require a _____ (small, large) amount of energy to

⟱ jump to the conduction band.

small

65

With a _____ (large, small) amount of energy the excess electrons in an extrinsic semiconductor will jump from their energy level in the

⇩ _____ band to the _____ band.

small
forbidden
conduction

Which requires the smaller applied energy:
(1) to force an electron from the valence band to the conduction band, or
(2) to force an electron from its energy level in the forbidden band to the conduction band?

⇩

(2)

Conduction will occur when electrons are in the conduction band. In an N-type extrinsic semiconductor, _____ (more, less) energy is required to provide conduction electrons than in an intrinsic

⇩ semiconductor.

less

Impurity atoms that provide excess electrons for conduction in N-type material are called *donor* atoms because they *donate* electrons to the conduction band. If an atom has 5 electrons and is added to an intrinsic semiconductor with 4 valence electrons, it is a

⇩ _____ atom.

donor

The operation of N-type semiconductor material depends on _____ atoms, which donate electrons to the conduction band.

⇩

donor

The excess electrons in N-type material appear in the forbidden band at a certain energy level, called the *donor level,* because electrons are donated from this _____ level to the conduction band.

⊽

donor

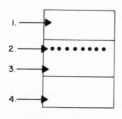

Figure 9

Refer to Figure 9. Here is an energy diagram of _____-type material. Supply the missing information.
(1) _____ band.   (2) _____ level.
(3) forbidden band.   (4) _____ band.

⊽

N
(1) conduction
(2) donor
(4) valence

Intrinsic semiconductor material appears in group IV of the periodic table because the outside electron shell contains _____ electrons. The donor atom for N-type extrinsic materials must come from group _____ since it contains 5 valence electrons.

⊽

4
V

The periodic table indicates that intrinsic semiconductor material comes from group _____ and the N-type impurity atoms (donor atoms) come from group _____.

⇨

IV
V

A small amount of impurity is satisfactory for most semiconductor applications. This means that most of the atoms in an extrinsic semiconductor crystal will be from group _____ in the periodic table.

⇨

IV

An N-type extrinsic semiconductor crystal is made from _____ material in group IV and _____ atoms from group V.

⇨

intrinsic
impurity (donor)

TAKE A BREAK HERE.

What would happen if an impurity atom from group III were added to intrinsic semiconductor material from group IV. Would you expect excess electrons to be present in the crystal? _____

⇨

Since atoms from Group III have only three valence electrons, there will certainly be no excess electrons.

Assume that an impurity atom with three electrons is placed into an intrinsic crystal. All 3 electrons will be shared with intrinsic atoms, but there will still be a deficiency of _____ (how many?) electron(s) in the crystal.

⇨

one

68

For each impurity atom containing three electrons there will be a(n) _____ (excess, deficiency) of one electron.

⟁

deficiency

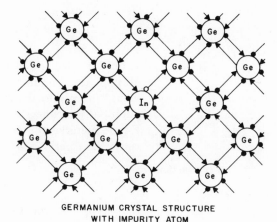

GERMANIUM CRYSTAL STRUCTURE
WITH IMPURITY ATOM

Figure 10

Figure 10 is a representation of a germanium crystal (intrinsic) with one impurity atom (3 valence electrons) placed in the crystal structure? There is a deficiency of _____ (how many?) electron(s).

1

When an extrinsic semiconductor has a deficiency of electrons it is a *P-type* semiconductor. An impurity atom with three valence electrons will cause a _____ (deficiency, excess) of electrons in a semiconductor; the crystal is a _____-type semiconductor.

deficiency
P

When an extrinsic semiconductor has a(n) _____ of electrons, it is P-type semiconductor material.

deficiency

69

_____-type material has a deficiency of electrons and is called _____-type because the absence of electrons in covalent crystals produces a

⊽ Positive charge.

P

P

It appears that a deficiency in electrons would probably hinder conduction, since not many electrons would jump into the _____ zone. This apparent discrepancy is explained by the fact that in P-type material the conduction zone is not used, because the electrons are not used for conduction.

⊽

conduction

In N-type material there is a(n) _____ of electrons; the conduction band is used for conduction. In P-type material there is a(n) _____ of electrons; the conduction band is *not* used for conduction.

⊽

excess
deficiency

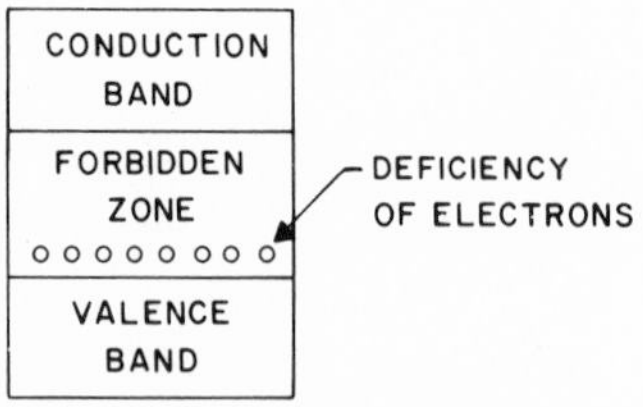

ENERGY DIAGRAM FOR
EXTRINSIC SEMI CONDUCTOR

Figure 11

70

Figure 11 shows the energy diagram for an extrinsic semiconductor with a deficiency of electrons; this would be the energy diagram for _____-type material.

⟁ *P*

P-type semiconductor material will have _____ (a higher, the same, a lower) number of electrons than an intrinsic semiconductor.

⟁ *a lower*

The energy diagram of an *intrinsic* semiconductor (no deficiency of electrons) has no place for electrons in the forbidden band. The energy diagram of a P-type *extrinsic* semiconductor (with a deficiency of electrons) _____ (does, does not) have an available energy level for electrons in the forbidden band.

⟁ *does*

The empty energy level or "holes" in the _____ band of a P-type energy diagram represent the absence of electrons.

⟁ *forbidden*

The "holes" in the forbidden band of a P-type semiconductor represent the _____ (excess, deficiency) of electrons caused by the impurity atoms having only _____ (how many?) valence electrons.

⟁ *deficiency*
3

The holes* caused by the impurity atoms appear on the energy diagram in the _____ band. Notice that the holes occur at one energy level and do not fill the band.

⇩ *one hole = one electron deficiency = one positive charge.

forbidden

Electrons have negative charges. A hole, or the deficiency of an electron, has a _____ charge.

⇩

positive

Where do the electron deficiencies (holes) in P-type material come from? _____. What charge is associated with a hole? _____.

⇩

P-type impurity atoms have only 3 valence electrons; but the atoms in the semiconductor crystal need to share four electrons for complete covalent bonds; hence electron deficiency.

positive

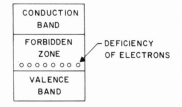

ENERGY DIAGRAM FOR
EXTRINSIC SEMI CONDUCTOR

Figure 11

The holes have an energy level close to the _____ (valence, conduction) band. An electron would jump from the _____ band to a hole if enough energy were applied.

⇩

valence
valence

Which requires less energy?
(1) to move an electron from the valence band to a hole, or
(2) to move an electron from the valence band to the conduction band.

⇩

(1)

A _____ (small, large) amount of energy
is required to move electrons from the valence band
⤵ to a hole.

small

In P-type material, when enough energy is added to
an electron in the valence band, the electron will
possess sufficient energy to occupy the hole energy
level. We say then that a hole has been "filled." What
remains in the original location of the electron? A
hole, of course. Every time an electron moves to fill
a hole, the _____ appears to move in a
⤵ reverse direction.

hole

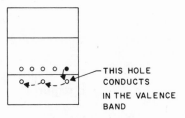

APPARENT MOVEMENT OF HOLES

Figure 12

Refer to Figure 12. When a hole in P-type material
is filled by an electron, the hole appears to move.
This apparent motion of holes is due to the fact that
when one electron acquires sufficient energy to fill
a hole, it leaves a hole which must be filled, etc.

⤵ *Proceed to next frame.*

In P-type material, electrons never reach the conduction band because they are always filling up
_____, which requires _____ (more, less) energy. In P-type material, there is no electron conduction. There is only conduction by
_____s, representing positive charges. (This
✧ is theoretically correct.)

holes
less
holes

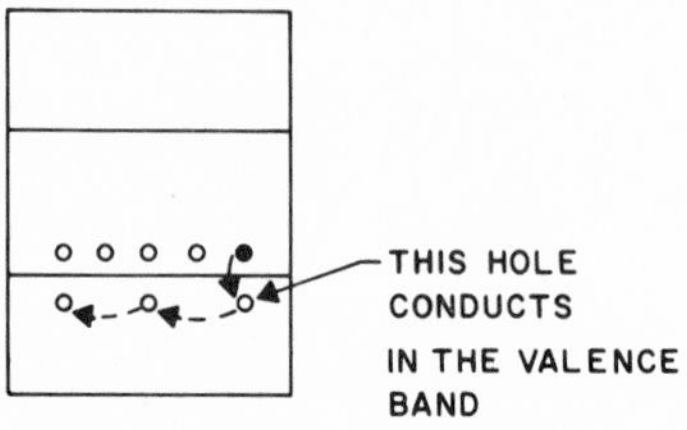

APPARENT MOVEMENT OF HOLES

Figure 12

Once a hole appears in the valence band (Figure 12), it requires a _____ (small, large) amount of energy to move it in a horizontal direction (remember, the energy scale is vertical). Therefore, most hole conduction will take place in the _____
✧ band because so little energy is required.

small
valence

In P-type semiconductor material, conduction takes place through the movement of _____s in the
_____ band. In N-type semiconductor material conduction takes place in the conduction band by movement of _____s which have jumped
✧ from the donor level.

holes
valence
electrons

In N-type material, electrons carry the conduction; electrons are called the *carriers*. In P-type material, holes carry the conduction. The carrier in P-type ⟳ material is the _____.

hole

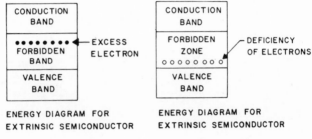

ENERGY DIAGRAM FOR   ENERGY DIAGRAM FOR
EXTRINSIC SEMICONDUCTOR   EXTRINSIC SEMICONDUCTOR

Figure 8   *Figure 11*

(1) In an intrinsic semiconductor, electrons must jump from the valence band to the conduction band for conduction to occur.

(2) In a P-type extrinsic semiconductor, electrons must jump from the valence band to a hole for conduction to occur.

Which requires *less* energy, (1) or (2)? Refer to ⟳ Figures 8 and 11 if necessary.

(2) from valence band to hole

Impurity atoms that provide holes for conduction in P-type material are called *acceptor* atoms because holes in the forbidden band *accept* electrons from the _____ band. If an atom has 3 electrons and is added to an intrinsic semiconductor, it will be a(n) ⟳ _____ (rejector, donor, acceptor) atom.

valence
acceptor

The operation of *P*-type semiconductor material depends on _____ atoms which accept electrons from the valence band. ⟳

acceptor

75

The holes in P-type material appear in the forbidden band at a certain energy level, called the *acceptor level*, because electrons are accepted at the

▽   _____ level from the valence band.

acceptor

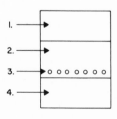

Figure 13

Refer to Figure 13. Here is an energy diagram of _____-type material. Supply the missing information.

(1) _____ Band.   (2) _____ Zone.

▽ (3) Acceptor level.   (4) _____ Band.

P

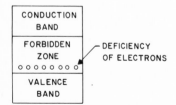

Acceptor atoms for P-type material have three valence electrons, so they will appear in group _____

▽ of the periodic table. Refer to the periodic table.

III

P-type impurity atoms (acceptors with three valence electrons) come from group _____; intrinsic semiconductor atoms (with four valence electrons) come from group _____; N-type impurity atoms (donors with five valence electrons) come from

⇩ group _____.

III
IV
V

In P-type semiconductors, _____ are the
⇩ basis for conduction.

holes

In N-type material, _____ are the basis for
⇩ conduction.

electrons

In intrinsic semiconductors, _____ are the
⇩ basis for conduction.

electrons

The two extrinsic semiconductor materials are the
⇩ _____-type and the _____-type.

N
P
(either order)

An acceptor atom, used as the impurity in
_____-type material, will have _____
⇩ (how many?) valence electrons.

P
3

A donor atom, used as the impurity in
_____-type material, will have _____
⇩ (how many?) electrons before it combines.

N
5

77

The _____ (intrinsic, extrinsic) semiconductor
requires the *least* applied energy for conduction.

Hint: Which type of semiconductor has donor or acceptor levels,
reducing the amount of applied energy for conduction?

⬦

extrinsic

Draw energy diagrams of P-type and N-type semiconductor material. Label zones, donor level, and acceptor
level.

⬦

N-type:

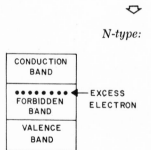

P-type:

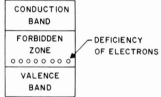

78

THE P-N JUNCTION

Separate crystals of P-type or N-type semiconductor material are not in themselves important. The combinations of the two types are useful. You would guess that a P-N diode was a combination of _____- type and _____-type crystals.

P

N

Almost all semiconductor devices in use today are combinations of the two types of extrinsic materials described previously (P-type and N-type). A P-N-P device would have two _____-type crystals and one _____-type crystal.

P

N

The simplest operating semiconductor device is a combination of one P-type crystal and one N-type crystal, called a P-N junction diode. A P-N junction diode _____ (can, cannot) be manufactured from all P-type material.

cannot

79

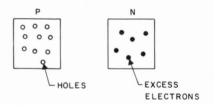

UNJOINED P AND N CRYSTAL

Figure 14

Refer to Figure 14. These two unjoined crystals will behave differently when joined. The left crystal is

⌤ _____-type; its carriers are _____.

P
holes

Let's examine the P-type crystal. Its carriers for conduction are _____ s. The impurities in P-type crystal are _____ (acceptor, donor) atoms which have _____ (how many?) valence ⌤ electrons.

holes
acceptor
3

An acceptor atom (as does any atom) has a net charge of _____ (0, +1, −1) before it is inserted as an impurity, because the number of ⌤ _____ is equal to the nuclear charge.

0
electrons

When the acceptor impurity atom accepts an electron from the intrinsic material (jumping up from the valence band), its net charge will be _____ (+1, −1, 0) because the additional electron is nega- ⌤ tive.

−1

When acceptor impurity atoms accept electrons, they become _____ (positively, negatively, neutrally) charged.

negatively

An impurity atom is a(n) _____ (acceptor, donor) atom if it becomes negatively charged during semiconductor operation.

acceptor

In the N-type crystal the current carriers are _____ (ions, electrons, holes). The impurities in N-type crystals are _____ (acceptor, donor) atoms which have _____ (how many?) valence electrons.

electrons
donor
5

A donor atom has a net charge of _____ before it is inserted as an impurity, because the number of electrons is equal to the nuclear charge.

0

In N-type material, when the donor atom gives up an electron to the conduction band, the net charge on the impurity atom will be _____ (+1, −1, 0) because it lost a negative charge.

+1

When a donor impurity atom donates an electron, it becomes _____ (positively, negatively, neutrally) charged.

positively

81

An impurity atom is a(n) _____ (acceptor, donor) atom if it becomes positively charged during semiconductor operation.

⟁

donor

Assume that the P-type and N-type material are brought together. At the junction there will be excess holes on the _____-type side and excess electrons on the _____-type side.

⟁

P

N

At the P-N junction, some of the _____ from the P-type crystal will combine with some of the _____ from the N-type crystal.

⟁

holes

electrons

If all the holes in the P-type material combine with excess electrons from the N-type material, there would be no more holes, and no more P-type material. Obviously, this _____ (does, does not) happen.

⟁

does not

At the P-N junction, let's assume that an excess electron from the N-side fills a hole on the P-side. When the donor impurity atom on the N-side lost the excess electron, it became _____ (positively, negatively) charged.

⟁

positively

The acceptor impurity atom on the P-side, the hole of which was filled, has gained an electron, so it becomes _____ (negatively, positively) charged.

⟁

negatively

An impurity atom is a(n) _____ (acceptor, donor) atom if it becomes negatively charged during semiconductor operation.

⬦

acceptor

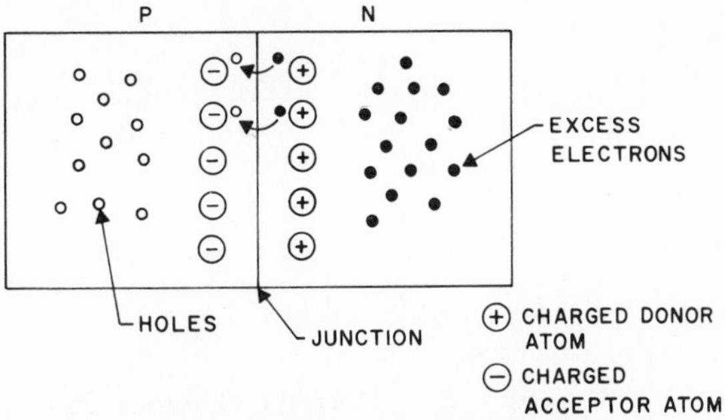

DIAGRAM SHOWING CHARGED IMPURITY ATOMS

Figure 15

The situation is thus (Refer to Figure 15): On the P-side in the region near the junction, there are _____ (acceptor, donor) impurity atoms which are _____ (positively, negatively, neutrally) charged because they each accepted an electron to fill a hole.

⬦

acceptor
negatively

On the N-side in the region near the junction, there are _____ (acceptor, donor) impurity atoms which are _____ (positively, negatively, neutrally) charged because they each donated a(n) _____ to fill a hole in the P-side.

⬦

donor
positively
electron

In the region around the junction, the P-type crystal contains _____ charged impurity atoms (acceptors). The N-type crystal contains _____ charged impurity atoms (donors).

⬦

negatively
positively

83

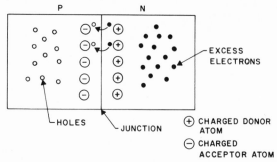

DIAGRAM SHOWING CHARGED IMPURITY ATOMS

Figure 15

As the distance increases away from the junction on the P-type side, we find _____ (more, fewer) holes which have combined with excess electrons from the N-type side since the immediate supply *at the junction* has _____ (increased, been depleted).

⇨

fewer
been depleted

Opposite charges will _____ (attract, repel) each other. Holes in the P-type will move toward the junction since they are _____ (positive, negative) and the acceptor impurities at the junction are _____ charged (have accepted electrons).

⇨

attract
positive
negatively (oppositely)

Electrons in the N-type material will move toward the junction since they are _____ (positive, negative) and the donor impurities at the junction are _____ charged (donated electrons).

⇨

negative
positively (oppositely)

Because the electrons are attracted toward the positive donor atoms on their side of the junction (N-side), they begin to move toward the junction; but the acceptor atoms on the P-side are _____ (positively, negatively) charged, and will _____ (help, prevent) the electrons from crossing the junction.

⇩

negatively
prevent

In the same manner, the positively charged *holes* will move toward the junction from the P-side, but will reach a point where the _____ (repulsion, attraction) of the donor atoms on the _____-type side is stronger than the _____ (attraction, repulsion) of the acceptor atoms on the _____-type side.

⇩

repulsion
N
attraction
P

After enough excess electrons have filled enough holes at the junction, the junction is charged and combinations no longer take place. No more _____ will approach the junction from the P-type side and no more _____ will approach the junction from the N-type side.

⇩

holes
electrons

When P-type and N-type materials are placed together to form a P-N junction, holes and excess electrons from the crystals _____ (do, do not) cancel each other by combining at the junction until an equilibrium condition is reached.

⇩

do

In a P-N junction, _____ (all, some, none) of the excess electrons on the N-side combine with holes on the P-side.

▽

some

The more charged impurity atoms (acceptor and donor) that exist at the P-N junction, the _____ (more, less) tendency excess electrons have to cross the junction.

▽

less

When an excess electron combines with a hole at a P-N junction, two charged impurity atoms are formed, one on each side of the junction. The presence of these charged atoms _____ (increases, decreases, has no effect on) the number of combinations between holes and electrons that take place after the original combination.

▽

decreases

The number of combinations between holes and electrons is limited because of two reasons:
(1) electrons on the N-side are prevented from crossing the junction by the charged _____ (donor, acceptor) atoms on the _____-side and
(2) holes on the P-side are repelled from the junction by the charged _____ (donor, acceptor) atoms on the _____-side.

▽

acceptor
P
donor
N

Donor impurities are associated with _____-type material. When a donor impurity atom donates an electron, the atom assumes a _____ charge. That charged donor impurity atom will repel a hole (positive charge) in _____-type material on the other side of a P-N junction.

⬦

N

positive

P

Acceptor impurities are associated with _____-type material. When an acceptor impurity atom accepts an electron, the atom assumes a _____ charge. That charged acceptor impurity atom will repel an electron in _____-type material on the other side of a P-N junction.

⬦

P

negative

N

A P-N junction is composed of two semiconductor crystals, one _____-type and one _____-type.

⬦

N

P

(either order)

In a P-N junction, as in separate P and N crystals, the conduction carrier for N-type crystal is the _____and for the P-type crystal is the _____.

⬦

electron

hole

BIASED P-N JUNCTIONS

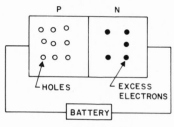

BIASED P-N JUNCTION

Figure 16

If an external voltage is applied across the P-N junction, the junction will be biased. If a battery were connected as in Figure 16, the P-N junction would be

⇩   _____.

biased

⇩   A junction is _____ when an external voltage is applied across it.

biased

⇩   A junction is _____ when an external _____ is applied across it.

biased
voltage

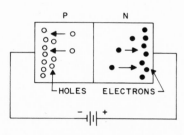

REVERSE BIASED JUNCTION

Figure 17

Assume that a battery is connected across the P-N junction diode so that the *P-side* is connected to the negative terminal. The holes (positive) in the P-type material will be _____ (attracted to, repelled from) the negative terminal. (See Figure 17.)

attracted to

The positive terminal of the battery is connected to the N-side of the junction. The electrons in the N-type material will be _____ (attracted to, repelled from) the positive terminal.

attracted to

If a P-N junction is biased by a battery and the negative terminal is at the P-side, the _____ s in the P-material will be attracted to the negative terminal. The _____ s in the N-side will be attracted to the positive terminal.

holes
electrons

If the holes in the P-type and the electrons in the N-type are pulled away from the junction (because of a battery across the P-N junction diode) then the conduction carriers _____ (can, cannot) cross the junction.

cannot

If conduction carriers do not cross the P-N junction, conduction _____ (can, cannot) take place across the junction.

cannot

When a negative terminal is attached to the P-side and a positive terminal is attached to the N-side, the current carriers, _____ s in the P-side and _____ s in the N-side, are pulled

⌂ _____ (away from, toward) the junction.

holes
electrons
away from

Because the current carriers are pulled away from the junction, they cannot cross the junction. A conduction carrier _____ (must, must not) cross the

⌂ junction for conduction to take place.

must

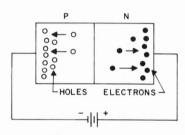

REVERSE BIASED JUNCTION

Figure 17

Refer to Figure 17. With the external voltage applied as shown, will there be conduction across the P-N

⌂ junction?_____.

No. No current carriers
cross the junction.

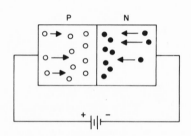

FORWARD BIASED JUNCTION

Figure 18

If we reversed the terminals of the external bias battery shown in Figure 17, the positive terminal would appear on the _____-side and the negative terminal would appear on the _____-side. This arrangement is shown in Figure 18.

⊽

P

N

When the positive terminal is attached to the P-side, the positively charged holes will be _____ (repelled from, attracted toward) the positive terminal and travel to the junction.

⊽

repelled from

When the negative terminal is attached to the N-side, the negatively charged electrons will be _____ (repelled, attracted) toward the P-N junction.

⊽

repelled

When a positive terminal is connected to the P-side and a negative terminal is connected to the N-side, the conduction carriers (holes and electrons) are forced toward the _____.

⊽

P-N junction

The external bias as shown in Figure 18 will force the conduction carriers to the P-N junction. When a hole and an electron meet at the junction, they _____ (combine, turn around, become confused).

⊽

combine

What happens when a hole and an electron combine at the junction? The electron jumps across the junction to fill the hole. If an electron crosses the P-N junction, we have conduction, and the conduction carrier is the _____.

⊽

electron

91

The _____ jumped across the junction from the N-side to the P-side, and was a conduction carrier.

electron

When an electron jumps from the _____-type to the _____-type across the _____ to fill a hole, _____ takes place.

N
P
P-N junction
conduction

When an electron jumps across the junction to fill a hole in the P-side, what does it leave? It leaves a hole. The hole appears to move from the P-side across the junction to the _____.

N-side

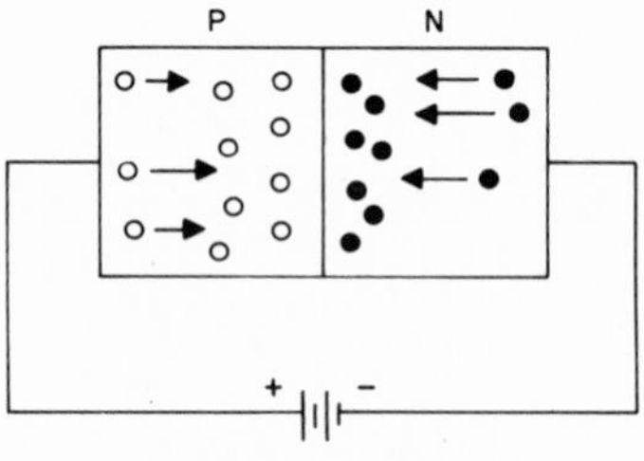

FORWARD BIASED JUNCTION

Figure 18

Since the hole moved across the P-N junction we have conduction and the conduction carrier is a hole. With a bias as indicated in Figure 18, we have conduction by both _____s and _____s.

electron
holes
(either order)

92

When a P-N junction conducts, _____ and _____ cross the junction. These current carriers cross the junction _____ (in the same direction, in the opposite directions).

↴

holes
electrons
(either order)
in opposite directions

Holes cross the junction from _____-type to _____-type. Electrons cross the junction from _____-type to _____-type. Acceptor, donor, and semiconductor atoms _____ (do, do not) cross the junction because they form the crystal structure.

P to N
N to P
do not

With a positive terminal on the P-side, the holes are repelled _____ (away from, toward) the terminal, and travel toward the _____.

away from
junction

With a _____ terminal on the N-side, the electrons are repelled toward the junction where they combine with _____s.

negative
holes

The combination of holes and electrons at the P-N junction constitute conduction; _____ (only electrons, only holes, both holes and electrons) cross the junction.

both holes and electrons

Conduction takes place at a junction when conduction carriers _____ the junction.

cross

Doesn't the N-type material run out of electrons to jump across the junction? No, because it is connected to the _____ terminal of a battery supply which supplies any number of electrons necessary.

negative

And why doesn't the P-type material run out of holes? The P-type material is connected to the _____ terminal of a battery supply; this terminal creates holes by taking away electrons.

positive

_____ are supplied at the negative terminal. They travel across the _____-type material, jump across the _____, filling the _____ on the P-side.

Electrons
N
junction
holes

_____ are created at the positive terminal. They travel across the _____-type material, and are filled at the _____, and appear to jump across it.

Holes
P
junction

A P-N junction which has a positive potential on its P-side and a negative potential on its N-side
⇩ _____ (will, will not) conduct.

will

When a junction is biased so that it will conduct, it is *forward biased*. A positive potential on the P-material and a negative potential on the N-material means
⇩ that the junction is _____ biased.

forward

When a junction is _____ it will conduct. Would you expect a *reverse* biased junction to con-
⇩ duct? _____ (yes or no).

forward biased
No. A reverse bias means that bias polarity is reversed. It won't conduct.

A _____ biased junction will not conduct. Its bias polarity is reversed from that of forward bias, so the positive terminal is connected to the
_____ -type side and the negative terminal
⇩ is connected to the _____ -type side.

reverse
N
P

The two bias conditions that can be applied to a P-N junction are the:
(1) _____ bias which will allow conduction
⇩ (2) _____ bias which will prevent conduction

Forward
Reverse

TRANSISTORS VS. ELECTRON TUBES

A. General

The transistor, like the electron tube, is a valve which controls the flow of current carriers (electrical charges in motion) through the semiconductor crystal material of which it is made. As the current carriers pass through the transistor, they are controlled as easily as if the same current carriers were passing through an electron tube. The transistor's ability to control current carriers and associated voltages makes it potentially the most useful single element in modern electronic equipment.

B. Transistors vs. Electron Tubes

(1) Efficiency and voltage requirements. The transistor power efficiency is greater than that of the electron tube because the transistor does not require heater power. In addition, it does not require warmup time, and it does not require a large dc voltage to operate.

(2) Useful life. Life expectancy is a very important consideration in the application of any electronic device. A transistor that is hermetically sealed in glass or metal will withstand a variety of situations that an electron tube cannot withstand. For example, a transistor, even though it is immersed in water, will operate for long periods of time with very little noticeable effect on its operating frequency. It also will withstand cen-

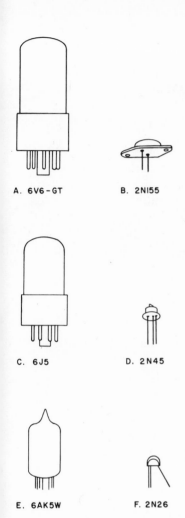

A. 6V6-GT

B. 2N155

C. 6J5

D. 2N45

E. 6AK5W

F. 2N26

COMPARISON OF TRANSISTORS AND
ELECTRON TUBES

Figure 1

trifugal force, gravity, and impact tests that would completely shatter an electron tube. It has been estimated that they can operate continuously for approximately 8 years, a time much greater than the life of the average electron tube.

(3) Noise level. The noise level of a transistor is approximately 20 db with a frequency input of 1,000 cycles per second. In comparison, the average electron tube has a lower noise level for the same frequency input. Although the noise level of a transistor is higher than that of an electron tube at this frequency, the noise level of the transistor is inversely proportional to the audio-frequency input. When a transistor is used with a higher frequency input, the noise level becomes considerably lower.

(4) Size and construction. A power amplifier electron tube is shown in Figure 1a, and a power amplifier transistor is shown in Figure 1b. The construction of the electron tube permits efficient dissipation of heat. Although the transistor must also dissipate heat, the size is noticeably smaller. The flange type construction of the transistor cover provides heat dissipation. In some cases a special metallic heat dissipator must be used. A medium power electron tube is shown in Figure 1c, and a medium power transistor is shown in Figure 1d. Note that the construction of the electron tube is much larger than that of the transistor. A miniature electron tube and a miniature transistor are shown in Figure 1e and f. The construction of the electron tube is again much larger than that of the transistor. Notice that the power transistor (Figure 1b) is smaller than the miniature electron tube (Figure 1e).

13 TRANSISTORS: WHAT THEY ARE AND HOW THEY WORK

A transistor is a semiconductor device using two P-N junctions. A P-N junction must be properly biased to operate. A transistor (two P-N junctions) must be properly _____ d to operate.

↔

biased

A transistor has _____ (how many?) biased P-N junctions.

↔

two

The _____ is a semiconductor device which has two P-N junctions. These junctions must be _____ (heated, cooled, biased, reversed) for operation.

↔

transistor
biased

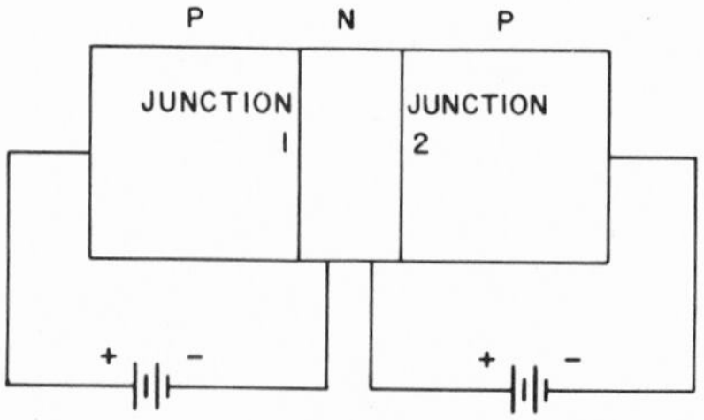

Figure 19

Let's assume the following configuration of semiconductor materials: an N-type material sandwiched between two P-type materials. See Figure 19. There are

▽ _____ (how many?) P-N junctions.

two

Each junction of a transistor must be biased in a particular way for proper operation. If forward biased, when a positive terminal is connected to the P-type and a negative terminal is connected to the N-type, conduction _____ (will, will not)

▽ occur.

will

Refer to Figure 19. Conduction _____ (will, will not) occur across P-N junction 1. Conduction _____ (will, will not) occur across P-N

▽ junction 2.

will
will not

Figure 19 shows the proper bias configuration for operation of the transistor. Let's examine the operation in detail. Holes will cross junction 1 from _____ (left to right, right to left). Electrons are crossing junction 1 in the _____ (same,

▽ opposite) direction.

left to right
opposite

Once the holes enter the N-type material, they can proceed to one of two places—either to the negative terminal on the N-type material or to the _____-type material on the other side of

▽ junction 2.

P

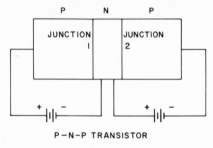

P-N-P TRANSISTOR

Figure 19

⌁ The holes coming across junction 1 can go either to the negative terminal on the _____-type material or travel across _____.

N
junction 2

⌁ When a P-N junction is forward biased it conducts heavily; this means that the holes and electrons will travel _____ (rapidly, slowly).

rapidly

⌁ The holes are traveling so _____ly when they arrive in the N-material from junction 1 that most of them go across junction _____. (Another reason is because the center section is very narrow.)

rapidly
2

⌁ The _____s coming across junction 1 can go either to the negative terminal or across _____. Most of them go across _____.

holes
junction 2
junction 2

Once a hole arrives across junction 2, it _____
(will, will not) be attracted by the negative terminal

↶ attached to the P-material.

will

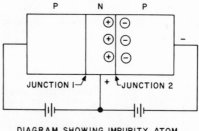

DIAGRAM SHOWING IMPURITY ATOM

Figure 20

Refer to Figure 20. Assume that a hole is just crossing
junction 2. This positively charged hole will be
_____ (repelled, attracted) by the positive

↶ charged donor atoms in the N-type material.

repelled

When crossing junction 2, the positive charged hole
will be _____ (repelled, attracted) by the
negative charged acceptor atoms in the P-type material and by the negative terminal on the P-type mate-

↶ rial.

attracted

Since conduction carriers are crossing junction 2,
_____ takes place even though the second

↶ junction is reverse biased.

conduction

Junction 1 is _____ biased.
↶ Junction 2 is _____ biased.

forward
reverse

101

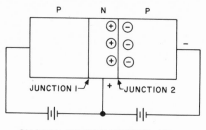

DIAGRAM SHOWING IMPURITY ATOM

Figure 20

The holes travel so fast across the forward biased junction _____ that they drift through the N-type material and cross reverse biased junction

⟳

_____.

1
2

A forward biased junction _____ (conducts, does not conduct) and shows a _____ (high, low) resistance.

⟳

conducts
low

A forward biased junction has a _____ (high, low) resistance. A reverse biased junction normally _____ (does, does not) conduct, and has a _____ (high, low) resistance.

⟳

low
does not
high

A _____ biased junction has a high resistance.

⟳

reverse

_____ (Almost all, Some, Almost none) of the holes crossing junction 1 also cross junction 2 because they are traveling rapidly.

⟳

Almost all

102

Since almost all of the holes crossing junction 1 cross, _____, almost the same conduction ⟳ exists throughout the transistor.

junction 2

Almost all of the holes that cross junction 1 also cross junction 2. But junction 1 has a _____ re- sistance because it is _____ biased, and junction 2 has a _____ resistance because ⟳ it is _____ biased.

low
forward
high
reverse

When a current (conduction carriers) crosses a low resistance, there is a _____ (high, low) voltage drop. When conduction carriers cross a high resistance, there is a _____ (high, low) ⟳ voltage drop.

low
high

When the holes (conduction carriers), which consti- tute a _____ (resistance, voltage, current) cross junction 1 (low resistance), a _____ ⟳ (high, low) voltage drop is produced.

current
low

The major current in a P-N-P transistor (crossing junction 1 and junction 2 in that order) is composed ⟳ of _____ s. They are called *majority carriers*.

holes

103

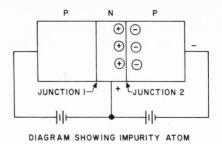

DIAGRAM SHOWING IMPURITY ATOM

Figure 20

⇨

1
2

The majority carriers in a transistor cross junction _____ and then cross junction _____.

⇨

majority

When a conduction carrier crosses junctions 1 and 2 in that order, it is a _____ (minority, majority, plurality) carrier.

⇨

high
high

When the holes cross junction 2, _____ (high, low) resistance, a _____ (high, low) voltage drop is produced.

⇨

holes
low
low
high
high

In the P-N-P transistor example, the current (composed of majority carriers called _____) crosses the _____ (high, low) resistance junction 1 causing a _____ voltage drop and also crosses _____ (high, low) resistance junction 2 causing a _____ voltage drop.

If the current through junction 1 can be changed, the current through junction 2 will _____ (change, not change).

⇩

change

If there is a change of current through the transistor, the voltage drops across the junctions _____ (will, will not) change.

⇩

will

When the current through the transistor changes, the voltage drop across the junctions _____. Since the resistance of junction 2 is _____ than the resistance of junction 1, the voltage drop across junction 2 will be _____ (more than, less than, equal to) the voltage drop across junction 1.

⇩

changes
higher
more than

If a small voltage change at junction 1 is accompanied by a larger voltage change at junction 2, a transistor can act as a(n) _____ (transmitter, amplifier, rectifier).

⇩

amplifier

A transistor can act as a(n) _____ because a small voltage change at junction 1 can effect a _____ (smaller, larger, equal) voltage change at junction 2.

⇩

amplifier
larger

We have examined the operation of a P-N-P transistor. Transistors can also be made with a P-type material sandwiched between two N-type materials. This

↻ would be an N-_____-N type transistor.

P

In an N-P-N transistor, as in a P-N-P, junction 1 must be _____ biased and junction 2 must be

↻ _____ biased for proper operation.

forward
reverse

An N-P-N transistor operates like the P-N-P transistor except that the majority conduction carriers are electrons. Since electrons are oppositely charged from holes, you would expect the bias voltage to be _____ (reversed, the same, randomly differ-

↻ ent) from P-N-P bias voltages.

reversed

Two types of transistors are the ____ - ___ and _____ - ___ - ___ . The two types both require a forward biased 1 junction and a reverse biased 2 junction, but the voltages applied will be of _____ (the

↻ same, opposite) polarity in the two types.

N-P-N ⎫
P-N-P ⎬ *either order*
　　⎭
opposite

An N-P-N transistor uses _____ as majority carriers. A P-N-P transistor uses _____ as majority carriers. Both transistors _____ (will, will not) amplify a small voltage change to a

↻ large voltage change.

electrons
holes
will

106

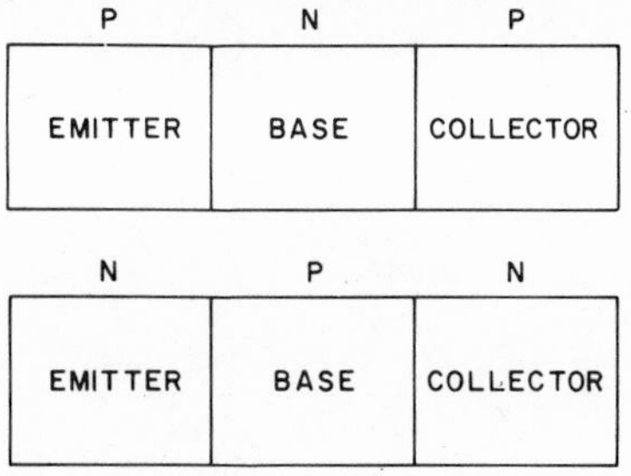

```
        P            N            P
   ┌──────────┬──────────┬──────────┐
   │          │          │          │
   │ EMITTER  │   BASE   │ COLLECTOR│
   │          │          │          │
   └──────────┴──────────┴──────────┘

        N            P            N
   ┌──────────┬──────────┬──────────┐
   │          │          │          │
   │ EMITTER  │   BASE   │ COLLECTOR│
   │          │          │          │
   └──────────┴──────────┴──────────┘
```

THREE PARTS OF TRANSISTORS

Figure 21

Refer to Figure 21; these are the three parts of a transistor. The middle part separating junctions 1 and 2 is called the base. The material separating junctions 1 and 2 in a P-N-P transistor is _____-type material and is called the _____.

N

base

In an N-P-N transistor, the sandwiched part is _____-type material. It is called the _____.

P

base

The material forming junction 1 with the base is called the *emitter*. The _____ and the base form junction 1.

emitter

The majority carriers originate in the _____ which forms junction 1 with the base. These current carriers are *emitted* across junction 1.

emitter

107

The _____ of a transistor originates the majority carriers which cross junction 1 into the _____ of the transistor.

☞

emitter
base

The emitter and base of a transistor are made of the same type of material. True or false? _____.

☞

false

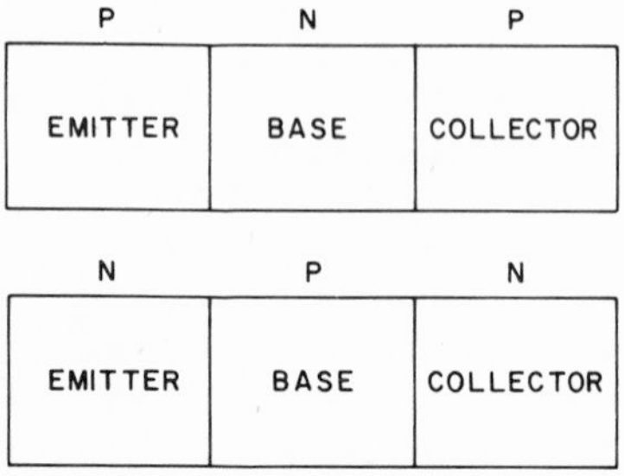

P	N	P
EMITTER	BASE	COLLECTOR

N	P	N
EMITTER	BASE	COLLECTOR

THREE PARTS OF TRANSISTORS

Figure 21

The part of a transistor which forms junction 2 with the base is called the collector because it collects the conduction carriers. The emitter emits the majority carriers and the _____ collects the carriers.

☞

collector

☞ The base is between the emitter and _____.

collector

The emitter and base form junction _____.
☞ The base and collector form junction _____.

1
2

The three parts of any transistor are the _____, base, and _____.

☞

emitter
collector

108

Draw a P-N-P transistor. Label the P and N materials. Label the base, emitter, and collector.

⬇

A P-N-P transistor:

P	N	P
EMITTER	BASE	COLLECTOR

Draw a P-N-P transistor. Show the direction of hole travel when junction 1 is forward biased.

⬇

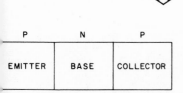

The holes travel from emitter to collector.

109

Draw an N-P-N transistor; label N and P materials, emitter, base, and collector. Show the direction of electron travel when the junction 1 is forward biased.

▽

An N-P-N transistor:

N	P	N
EMITTER	BASE	COLLECTOR

Electrons travel from emitter to collector.

There is an emitter, a collector, and a base in
_____ (N-P-N, P-N-P, N-P-N and P-N-P) transistors. The emitter of an N-P-N transistor
_____ (does, does not) perform the same function as the emitter of a P-N-P transistor (provides current carriers).

▽

N-P-N and P-N-P
does

Majority carriers travel from the _____ across the _____ to the _____ of a transistor.

▽

emitter
base
collector

110

Draw a properly biased N-P-N transistor.

Hint: Remember that polarities must be opposite those of a properly biased P-N-P transistor.

A properly biased N-P-N transistor:

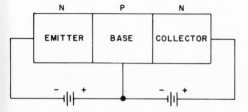

set # 14   **IMPORTANCE OF MINORITY CARRIERS**

Ideally, a P-N diode should have zero resistance when forward biased and infinite resistance when _____ biased. In an actual transistor these

↴   ideal conditions cannot be attained.

reverse

A reverse biased P-N junction _____ (does,

↴   does not) have infinite resistance.

does not

A P-N junction cannot have infinite resistance when it is reverse biased because of the presence of *minority carriers*, which occur in small numbers in semiconductor materials. Transistors contain

↴   _____.

minority carriers

Minority carriers occur in semiconductor materials in small numbers as compared to majority conduction carriers. _____ (Less, More) conduction can occur with minority carriers than with majority

↴   conduction carriers.

Less

The majority carriers in a P-type material are holes. The minority carriers in P-type material are oppositely charged carriers, so the minority carriers in a P-type material are negative. Can you think of a

↴   negative carrier? _____.

electron

The minority carriers in P-type material are electrons and are oppositely charged from the majority carriers, or _____s.

holes

The small number of free electrons that appear in P-type material are _____. They are present because a covalent bond occasionally breaks and releases the electron.

minority carriers

Minority carriers are oppositely charged from the regular (majority) conduction carriers, so they will travel in the _____ (same direction as, opposite direction from) regular carriers.

opposite direction from

In a reverse biased P-N junction, the regular carriers (holes) on the P side will not cross the junction from P to N. The minority carriers _____ (will, will not) cross the junction.

will

Since there are a small number of electrons in P-type material coming from an occasional breaking of covalent bonds (or stray electrons), there will be _____ (high, low) conduction across the junction when it is reverse biased.

low

If low conduction occurs across the reverse biased junction, it means that _____ (high, low) resistance, but not infinite resistance, exists at the junction.

high

In P-type material, the majority carriers are
_____ s and the minority carriers are

▽ _____ s.

holes
electrons

In N-type material the majority carriers are electrons.
You would expect the minority carriers to be

▽ _____ s.

holes

In a reverse biased junction, electrons will not travel
from N-type material to P-type material. The minority
carriers, which are _____ s in N-type mate-

▽ rial, will cross the junction.

holes

In a reverse biased P-N junction, the majority carriers on one side will not carry the current and hence
_____ (do, do not) cross the junction. The
minority carriers do carry the current and cross the

▽ junction.

do not

In a *reverse biased* P-N junction, the minority carriers, or _____, in the P-side _____
(do, do not) cross into the N-side; the majority carriers, or _____, in the P-side _____

▽ (do, do not) cross into the N-side.

electrons
do
holes
do not

114

In a reverse biased P-N junction, the minority carriers, or _____, in the N-side _____ (do, do not) cross into the P-side; the majority carriers, or _____, in the N-side _____ (do, do not) cross into the P-side.

holes
do
electrons
do not

The resistance of a reverse biased P-N junction _____ (is, is not) infinite because of the presence of a small number of minority carriers.

is not

PART TWO

TRANSISTOR SYMBOLS

SYMBOLS AND MANUFACTURERS' NOMENCLATURE

Symbols are the shorthand of professional people. In the field of transistors there exists a variety of symbols the knowledge of which is necessary in circuit analysis. This set will familiarize you with these symbols.

▽ *Proceed to next frame.*

The P-N-P transistor symbol has an arrow pointing toward the base, or as generally said, "pointing in." The symbol

▽ represents a transistor of the _____ type.

P-N-P

Let's look at the symbol for a P-N-P transistor.

The slanted line with the arrow is the emitter; the collector is on the right side and does not show an arrow; and the base is the horizontal line.

▽ *Proceed to next frame.*

The symbol

represents the _____ of a P-N-P transistor. The symbol

represents the _____ of a P-N-P transistor. The horizontal line below both of these symbols rep-
▽ resents the _____ of a P-N-P transistor.

emitter
collector
base

119

A P-N-P transistor has the arrow on the emitter pointing toward the base. Complete the symbol to show a P-N-P transistor.

The P-N-P transistor symbol is not complete because the _____ is missing.

base

The arrow on the emitter of a P-N-P transistor symbol is pointing _____ the base.

toward

Complete the following P-N-P transistor symbol:

Complete the following P-N-P transistor symbol:

Draw a P-N-P transistor symbol and label each part.

EMITTER

BASE

COLLECTOR

The N-P-N transistor symbol is similar to the P-N-P symbol, but the arrow on the emitter is reversed. The following N-P-N symbol does not show the emitter. Complete the symbol.

The emitter of an N-P-N transistor symbol has its arrow pointing _____ (toward, away from) the base.

away from

Draw an N-P-N transistor and label each part.

EMITTER
BASE
COLLECTOR

(1) The following is a(n) _____ type transistor:

(2) The following is a(n) _____ type transistor:

(1) P-N-P
(2) N-P-N

The symbol for a crystal diode is as follows:

The arrow symbolizes the plate while the perpendicular line symbolizes the cathode.

Proceed to the next frame.

121

The following symbol shows an incomplete diode.

——▶——

The plate is shown but not the _____. Complete the symbol.

cathode

——▶|——

The following symbol shows an incomplete diode.

———|——

The cathode is shown but not the _____.
Complete the symbol.

plate

——▶|——

Draw the symbol for a diode and label each part.

———CATHODE
PLATE———▶|——

The direction of the arrow indicates the direction of
holes or conventional current flow. Electron flow is
opposite to the flow of holes or conventional current
flow. Electrons in a diode or transistor will therefore
flow _____ (with, against) the arrow.

against

This is the symbol for a(n) _____ type
transistor. Electrons will flow _____ (with,
against) the arrow.

P-N-P
against

122

This symbol represents a(n) _____ type transistor. Electrons will flow _____ (with, against) the arrow.

N-P-N
against

Electrons in the following diode will flow from the _____ (left, right) to the _____ (left, right).

right
left

As in tube designations, numbers in transistors have a definite meaning. The first number followed by a letter tells us whether this is a transistor or diode. 2N indicates a transistor and 1N a diode. The designation 2N393 indicates a _____.

transistor

If you find the designation 1N96 in a circuit, you will know that this is a(n) _____.

diode

Indicate whether the following are transistors or diodes:
2N 104 _____.
1N 21B _____.

transistor
diode

PART THREE

RECTIFICATION
AND AMPLIFICATION

1

RECTIFICATION/JUNCTION DIODE

Note: Throughout this program current flow means electron current flow (opposite of conventional current flow) unless otherwise stated.

The junction diode has the characteristics of *low forward* impedance and *high reverse* impedance. Current flowing through a junction diode in the forward direction would meet a _____ impedance and in the reverse direction would meet a _____

▽ impedance.

low
high

A junction diode has the characteristics of low _____ impedance and high _____

▽ impedance.

forward
reverse

Low impedance allows current flow and _____

▽ impedance prevents current flow.

high

A device that has a low forward impedance and high reverse impedance allows current to flow in *one* direction. A junction diode allows current to flow in

▽ _____ direction.

one

The process of allowing current to flow in one direction and not in the other direction is known as *rectification*. A junction diode can be used for

▽ r_____ of an AC signal.

rectification

127

Because of its characteristic low forward impedance and high reverse impedance, the junction diode can ▽ be used to _____ an AC signal.

rectify

The junction diode acts as a _____ because of its characteristic of _____ forward im- ▽ pedance and _____ reverse impedance.

rectifier
low
high

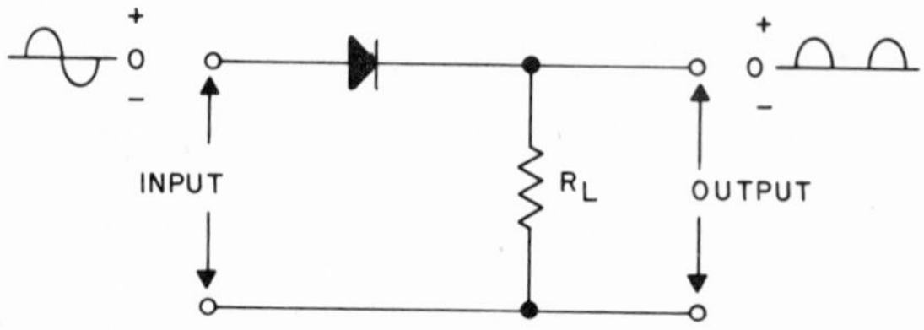

SIMPLIFIED RECTIFIER – POSITIVE OUTPUT

Figure 1

Figure 1 is a simplified half-wave diode rectifier. The input to the rectifier is a sine wave and the output ▽ consists of _____ (positive, negative) pulses.

positive

When the positive half of the sine wave is applied to the diode in Figure 1, it sees a low impedance and ▽ the current _____ (will, will not) flow.

will

When the negative half of the sine wave is applied to the diode in Figure 1, it sees a _____ ▽ impedance and the current will not flow.

high

128

As a result of the rectifying action as shown in Figure 1, the output is a series of _____ (positive, negative) pulses.

▽

positive

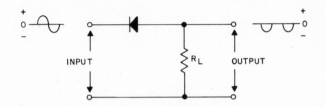

SIMPLIFIED RECTIFIER – NEGATIVE OUTPUT

Figure 2

The output as shown in Figure 2 is a series of

▽ _____ (positive, negative) pulses.

negative

You wish to remove the negative portion of an applied sine wave. The output would be a series of _____ pulses. Draw a simplified rectifier circuit to do this. Show the input and output waveforms.

▽

positive

Simplified rectifier-positive output:

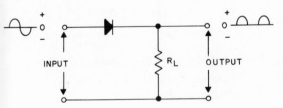

set **2**

BASIC CIRCUITS FOR AMPLIFICATION

Several circuit arrangements are possible for introducing a signal into a transistor and extracting a signal from the transistor. A transistor _____ (may, may not) be connected in more than one way for the introduction and extraction of a signal.

✧ *may*

Common base, common emitter, and *common collector* are possible circuit arrangements for introducing a signal into and extracting a signal from a transistor. Three possible transistor circuit arrangements are: common _____, common _____, and common _____.

✧

base
emitter
collector

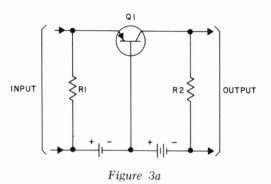

Figure 3a

Figure 3a is the circuit of a common-*base* amplifier. The element of the transistor which is common to the input and output circuits is the _____.

✧ *base*

130

If the base is the common element of the transistor, the input circuit consists of the emitter and base and the output circuit consists of the collector and

▽ ______________.

base

The signal is introduced into the emitter-base circuit

▽ and extracted from the ______________-base circuit.

collector

A circuit arrangement with the base of the transistor common to both input and output circuits is a com-

▽ mon-______________ amplifier.

base

▽ Figure 3a is a drawing of a _______-_______ amplifier.

common-base

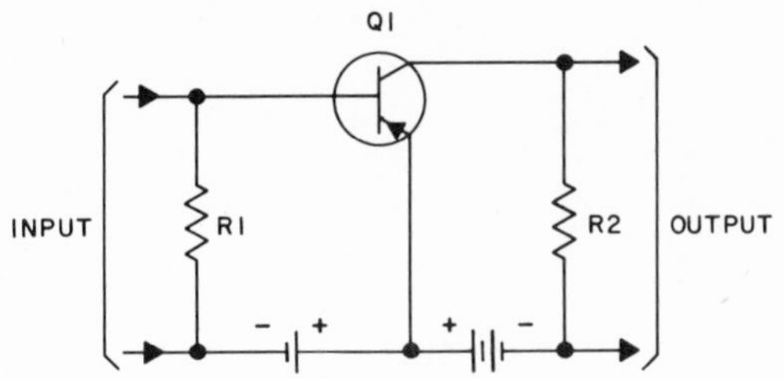

Figure 4a

Figure 4a is the circuit of a common-*emitter* amplifier. The element of the transistor which is common to

▽ the input and output circuits is the ______________.

emitter

If the emitter is the common element of the transistor amplifier, the input circuit consists of the base and emitter and the output circuit consists of the collector

▽ and ______________.

emitter

The signal is introduced into the base-emitter circuit and extracted from the _____-emitter circuit.

▽

collector

A circuit arrangement with the emitter of the transistor common to both input and output circuits is a _____-_____ amplifier.

▽

common-emitter

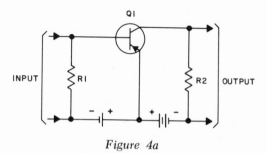

Figure 4a

▽ Figure 4a is a drawing of a _____-_____ amplifier.

common-emitter

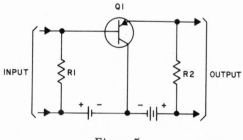

Figure 5a

Figure 5a is the circuit of a common-*collector* amplifier. The element of the transistor which is common to the input and output circuits is the

▽ _____.

collector

If the collector is the common element of the transistor amplifier, the input circuit consists of the base and collector and the output circuit consists of the emitter and _____.

collector

The signal is introduced into the base-collector circuit and is extracted from the _____-collector circuit.

emitter

A circuit arrangement with the collector of the transistor common to both input and output circuits is a _____-_____ amplifier.

common-collector

Figure 5a is a drawing of a _____-_____ amplifier.

common-collector

Three possible arrangements for transistor amplifiers are _____-_____ , _____-_____ , and _____-_____ .

common-base
common-emitter
common-collector

133

BIASING OF THE COMMON BASE AMPLIFIER

Although circuit arrangements may vary, proper biasing of a transistor amplifier consists of *forward* bias on the emitter-base circuit and *reverse* bias on the collector-base circuit. For proper biasing of a transistor amplifier, the emitter-base circuit must be _____ biased and the collector-base circuit must be _____ biased.

⇨

forward
reverse

A transistor amplifier in any circuit arrangement must have _____ bias on the emitter-_____ circuit and _____ bias on the collector-_____ circuit.

⇨

forward
base
reverse
base

The biasing requirements for transistor amplifiers are:
(1) _____ bias on the _____ - _____ circuit and
(2) _____ bias on the _____ - _____ circuit.

⇨

(1) forward
emitter-base
(2) reverse
collector-base

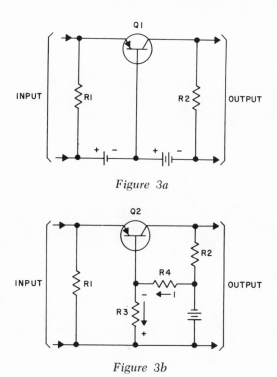

Figure 3a

Figure 3b

Figure 3a is an example of the use of *two* batteries for biasing a common-base amplifier and Figure 3b is an example of the use of *one* battery for biasing. The common-base amplifier may be biased with either _____ or _____ batteries.

one
two

A voltage divider using a resistor network is used to bias the common-base amplifier with a single battery. Biasing from a single battery is accomplished by dividing the _____.

voltage

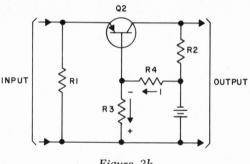

Figure 3b

The _____ divider for the single battery biased common-base amplifier (Figure 3b) consists of resistors R3 and R4.

◇

voltage

The resistor network R_____ and R_____ divides the _____ from the single battery to provide forward bias.

◇

R3
R4
voltage

The single battery provides reverse bias directly to the collector-base circuit, but uses the _____ divider to provide forward bias to the _____-base circuit.

◇

voltage
emitter

The voltage divider _____ biases the _____-base circuit.

◇

forward
emitter

In order to forward bias the emitter-base circuit, the base must be *negative* with respect to the emitter. The voltage divider places a _____ voltage on the base of the transistor.

◇

negative

136

The voltage divider insures that the base is

▽ _____ with respect to the _____.

negative
emitter

The voltage drop across resistor R3 is from

▽ _____ to _____. (Figure 3b)

negative
positive

The polarity of the voltage on the base is determined

▽ by the voltage drop across resistor _____.

R3

Reverse bias for the transistor in Figure 3b is
achieved by making the *collector* negative with respect to the *base*. Reverse bias is achieved directly

▽ by the battery in the _____-base circuit.

collector

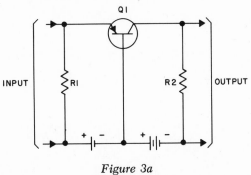

Figure 3a

In the common-base amplifier biased with two batteries (Figure 3a) forward bias is achieved directly
by the *battery* in the emitter-base circuit. Reverse
bias is achieved directly by the _____ in the

▽ collector-base circuit.

battery

137

A common-base amplifier using two batteries for biasing _____ (does, does not) require a voltage divider.

⌄

does not

A common-base amplifier biased with one battery _____ (does, does not) require a voltage divider.

⌄

does

In any transistor amplifier the emitter-base circuit must be _____ biased and the collector-base circuit must be _____ biased.

⌄

forward
reverse

BIASING OF THE COMMON-EMITTER AMPLIFIER

set

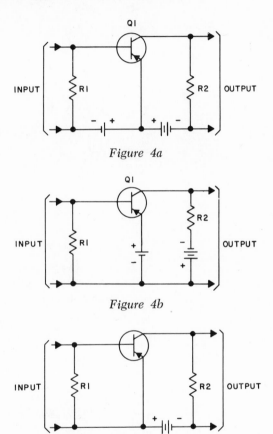

Figure 4a

Figure 4b

COMMON EMITTER AMPLIFIER

Figure 4c

Figures 4a, 4b, and 4c show biasing systems for a *common-emitter* amplifier. There are two, two-battery biasing systems for the _____ - _____ amplifier.

common-emitter

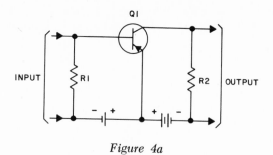

Figure 4a

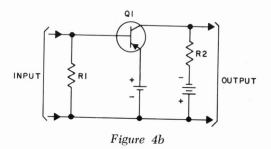

Figure 4b

Figures 4a and 4b show the _____ (how
many?) circuits using _____ (how many?)
batteries to bias the common-_____ amplifier.

two

two

emitter

The biasing method in Figure 4a is used if you want
to place the *emitter* at AC and DC ground potential
in an equipment. To place the _____ at AC
and DC ground potential, the biasing circuit in
Figure _____ is used.

emitter

4a

The circuit in Figure 4a places the emitter at
_____ and _____ ground potential.

AC

DC

The biasing method in Figure 4b is used if you want to have the base-emitter bias battery *aid* the collector-emitter battery. In order to have the base-emitter bias battery _____ the collector-emitter bias battery, the circuit in Figure 4b is used.

aid

The two methods of using two batteries for biasing a common-emitter amplifier are:
(1) placing the emitter at _____ and _____ground potential and
(2) having the base-emitter bias battery _____ the collector-emitter battery.

AC
DC
aid

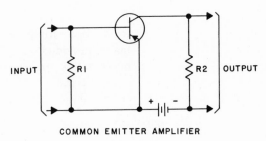

COMMON EMITTER AMPLIFIER

Figure 4c

The common-emitter amplifier can also be biased with a single battery. Figure 4c is an example of this arrangement.

Proceed to the next frame.

Refer to Figures 4a, 4b, and 4c. There are _____ (how many?) methods of biasing a common-emitter amplifier. Two methods use _____ (how many?) bias battery(ies) and one method uses _____ (how many?) bias battery(ies).

3
2
1

141

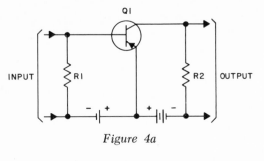

Figure 4a

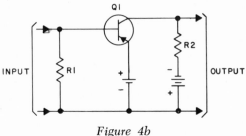

Figure 4b

In the two circuits using two bias *batteries,* forward bias is provided directly by the _____ in the base-emitter circuit and reverse bias is provided directly by the _____ in the _____-emitter circuit.

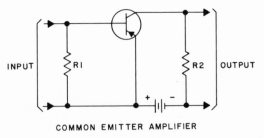

battery
battery
collector

COMMON EMITTER AMPLIFIER

Figure 4c

In the circuit using one bias battery, reverse bias is provided *directly* by the battery in the _____-emitter circuit.

collector

142

The *internal construction* of the transistor provides the required forward bias voltage in the base-emitter circuit. The common-emitter amplifier using one battery bias gets reverse bias directly from the bias battery but forward bias depends on the _____

⇲ _____ of the transistor.

internal construction

Forward bias requires the base of the transistor to be more *negative* than the emitter and reverse bias requires that the collector be more *negative* than the base. The collector, therefore, is at the highest _____ potential and the emitter is at the

⇲ lowest _____ potential.

negative
negative

To satisfy the requirement for forward bias of the transistor, the base must be _____ (more,

⇲ less) negative than the emitter.

more

To satisfy the requirement for reverse bias of the transistor, the collector must be _____

⇲ (more, less) negative than the base.

more

Physically, the base is located between the emitter and collector and therefore must assume a voltage between the two. The base assumes a voltage between the emitter and collector by being more _____ (negative, positive) than the emitter and less _____ (negative, positive) than the

⇲ collector.

negative
negative

143

⇨ The base must be _____ with respect to the emitter.

negative

⇨ The base must be less negative than the collector or, in other words, _____ with respect to the collector.

positive

⇨ Having the base negative with respect to the emitter satisfies the requirement of polarity necessary to produce a _____ bias.

forward

⇨ Having the collector negative with respect to the base satisfies the requirement of polarity necessary to produce _____ bias.

reverse

⇨ Because the common-emitter is a *voltage* amplifier, the magnitude of the _____ between the emitter and the base is small compared to that between the collector and the base.

voltage

⇨ The voltage between *the collector* and the base of a common-emitter amplifier is _____ (smaller, larger) than the voltage between the emitter and the base.

larger

⇨ Internally, the two P-N junctions act as a voltage divider. The P-N junction between the collector and the base represents a high resistance and develops the larger _____ drop.

voltage

144

The P-N junction between the emitter and base represents a low resistance and develops a low

▽ _____ drop.

voltage

Since there is a low voltage drop across the P-N junction between the _____ and base, and a high voltage drop across the P-N junction between the _____ and the base, the common-emit-

▽ ter arrangement acts as an amplifier.

emitter
collector

BIASING OF THE COMMON-COLLECTOR AMPLIFIER

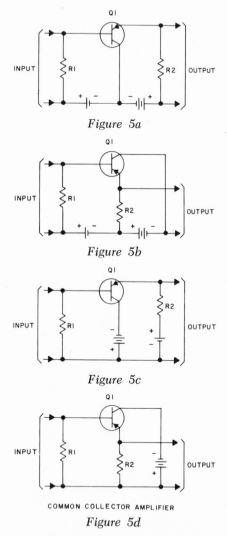

Figure 5a

Figure 5b

Figure 5c

COMMON COLLECTOR AMPLIFIER

Figure 5d

Figures 5a, 5b, 5c, and 5d illustrate four methods of biasing a *common-collector* amplifier. There are three (3) methods of introducing bias voltages from two batteries into the _____ - _____ amplifier.

▽

common-collector

Figures 5a, 5b, and 5c illustrate the biasing methods using _____ (how many?) battery(ies) for
⇩ the common-_____ amplifier.

2
collector

In each case the batteries establish the proper _____ and _____ biases for the
⇩ transistors.

forward
reverse

The common-collector amplifier can also be biased with a single *battery* as shown in Figure 5d. The _____ in the base-collector circuit provides
⇩ the _____ bias for the transistor.

battery
reverse

The forward bias depends on the internal structure of the transistor just as it does in the _____ - _____
⇩ amplifier.

common-emitter

There are _____ basic circuit configurations used for introducing signals to and extracting signals
⇩ from a transistor.

three

The three basic circuits are: _____ - _____ ,
⇩ _____ - _____ , and _____ - _____ .

common-base
common-emitter
common-collector

Either one or two batteries can be used to bias the
⊽ transistor in _____ (one, two, all) circuit(s).

all

In all circuits using two batteries, the _____
and _____ biases are established directly by
⊽ the batteries.

forward
reverse

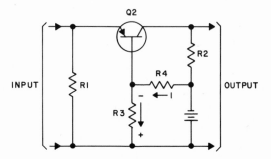

Figure 3b

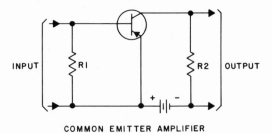

COMMON EMITTER AMPLIFIER

Figure 4c

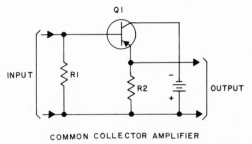

COMMON COLLECTOR AMPLIFIER

Figure 5d

148

Refer to Figures 3b, 4c, 5d. Each of these circuits uses _____ (how many?) battery(ies) for biasing. The circuits in Figure _____ (3b, 4c, 5d) use a voltage divider to establish _____ bias, and the circuits in Figures _____ and _____ (3b, 4c, 5d) depend on the internal structure of the transistor to establish forward bias.

⟳

one
3b
forward
4c and 5d

To establish forward bias the ____ - ____ amplifier uses a voltage divider and the ____ - ____ and ____ - ____ amplifiers use the internal structure of the transistor.

⟳

common-base
common-emitter
common-collector

set **CURRENT FLOW AND VOLTAGE PHASE RELATIONSHIPS; COMMON-BASE AMPLIFIER**

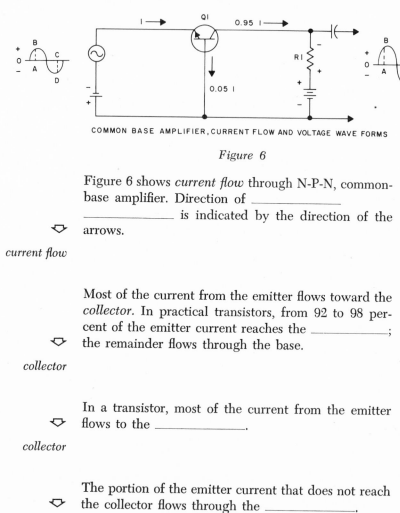

COMMON BASE AMPLIFIER, CURRENT FLOW AND VOLTAGE WAVE FORMS

Figure 6

Figure 6 shows *current flow* through N-P-N, common-base amplifier. Direction of _____

▽ _____ is indicated by the direction of the arrows.

current flow

Most of the current from the emitter flows toward the *collector*. In practical transistors, from 92 to 98 per-cent of the emitter current reaches the _____;

▽ the remainder flows through the base.

collector

In a transistor, most of the current from the emitter

▽ flows to the _____.

collector

The portion of the emitter current that does not reach

▽ the collector flows through the _____.

base

In Figure 6, the total emitter current is represented by the letter *I*. For discussion purposes, assume that 95 percent of the total emitter current reaches the collector. Therefore, _____ percent flows to the base.

⟱

5 percent

In Figure 6, 0.95 *I* represents the emitter current flowing to the _____, and 0.05 *I* represents the emitter current flowing to the _____.

⟱

collector
base

The waveforms shown in Figure 6 represent voltage waveforms. The input signal produced by the signal generator is on the left and the output signal developed across resistor R1 is on the right.

⟱ *Proceed to the next frame.*

When the positive portion of the input signal (AB) reaches the amplifier it *opposes* the forward bias produced by the emitter-base battery. The forward bias is _____ by the positive portion of the input signal.

⟱

opposed

When the positive portion of the input signal opposes the forward bias of the transistor, the resultant forward bias is reduced. This *reduction* in forward bias causes a similar _____ in the total current flow through the emitter.

⟱

reduction

151

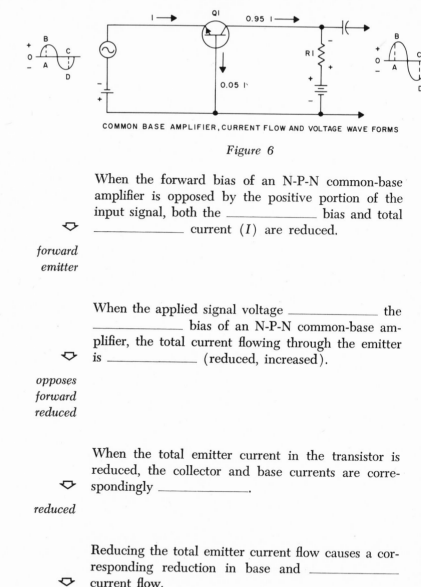

COMMON BASE AMPLIFIER, CURRENT FLOW AND VOLTAGE WAVE FORMS

Figure 6

When the forward bias of an N-P-N common-base amplifier is opposed by the positive portion of the input signal, both the _____ bias and total _____ current (*I*) are reduced.

forward
emitter

When the applied signal voltage _____ the _____ bias of an N-P-N common-base amplifier, the total current flowing through the emitter is _____ (reduced, increased).

opposes
forward
reduced

When the total emitter current in the transistor is reduced, the collector and base currents are correspondingly _____.

reduced

Reducing the total emitter current flow causes a corresponding reduction in base and _____ current flow.

collector

152

Reducing the collector current flow *reduces* the amount of current flow through resistor R1. The reduced current flow through R1 causes the top point to become less negative or more _____ with respect to the bottom point.

⇩

positive

When the flow of collector current is reduced, the top point of R1 becomes more _____.

⇩

positive

When the voltage at the top of R1 becomes more positive, the output voltage becomes more

⇩
_____.

positive

In an N-P-N common-base amplifier, the application of a positive input signal _____ the forward bias.

⇩

reduces (opposes)

A reduction in forward bias causes a reduction in total _____ current and in _____ and _____ currents.

⇩

emitter

base
collector } *(either order)*

A reduction in collector current flow causes the voltage at the top of R1 to become more _____ and results in a _____ (positive, negative) output voltage.

⇩

positive
positive

153

The application of a positive input signal to a common-base amplifier results in a _____ (positive, negative) output signal.

positive

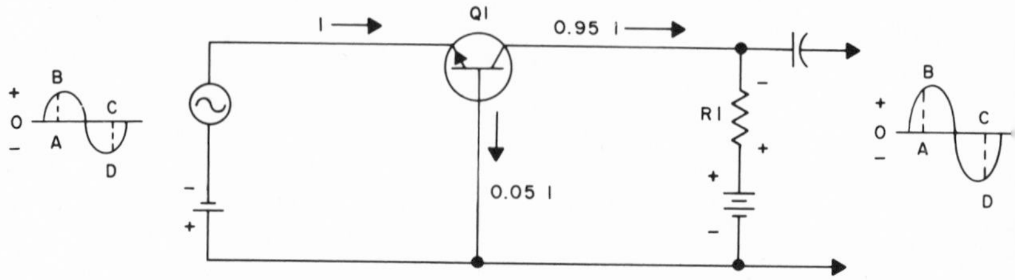

COMMON BASE AMPLIFIER, CURRENT FLOW AND VOLTAGE WAVE FORMS

Figure 6

When the negative portion of the input signal (*CD*) reaches the amplifier, it *aids* the forward bias. The forward bias is _____ ed by the negative portion of the input signal.

aided

When the forward bias is aided by the input signal, the resultant forward bias is increased. This increase in forward bias results in a similar increase in total _____ current.

emitter

When the forward bias of an N-P-N common-base amplifier is aided by the negative portion of the input signal, both the _____ bias and the total _____ current are increased.

forward
emitter

When the total emitter current is increased, the collector and base currents are _____.

increased

154

Increasing the total emitter current causes a corresponding increase in both _____ and _____ current flow.

⇩

base
collector
(either order)

Increasing the collector current flow increases the current flow through resistor R1. The increased current flow through R1 causes the top point of the resistor to become more _____ (negative, positive) with respect to the bottom point.

⇩

negative

When the voltage at the top of R1 becomes more negative, the output voltage becomes more _____.

⇩

negative

In an N-P-N common-base amplifier, the application of a negative input signal _____ the forward bias.

⇩

increases (aids)

An increase in forward bias causes an increase in total _____ current and in _____ and _____ currents.

⇩

emitter
base }
collector } *(either order)*

An increase in collector current flow causes the voltage at the top of R1 to become more _____ and results in a _____ (negative, positive) output voltage.

⇩

negative
negative

155

For the entire half cycle that the input signal goes positive, the output signal goes _____.

positive

For the entire half cycle that the input signal goes negative, the output signal goes _____.

negative

There _____ (is, is not) a voltage phase reversal between the input and output signals of a common-base amplifier.

is not

set 7   CURRENT FLOW AND VOLTAGE PHASE RELATIONSHIPS; COMMON-EMITTER AMPLIFIER

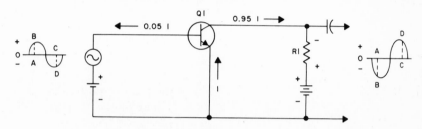

COMMON EMITTER AMPLIFIER, CURRENT FLOW AND VOLTAGE WAVE FORMS

Figure 7

Figure 7 shows electron *current* flow through an N-P-N common-emitter amplifier. Direction of _____ flow is indicated by the direction of the arrows.

⟱ *current*

The portions of the emitter current that flow through the base and collector are the same as those seen in the common-base amplifier, that is: 0.05 I and _____, respectively.

⟱ *0.95 I*

When the positive portion of the input signal (AB) reaches the amplifier it *aids* the forward bias produced by the base-emitter battery. The forward bias is _____ by the positive portion of the input signal.

⟱ *aided*

157

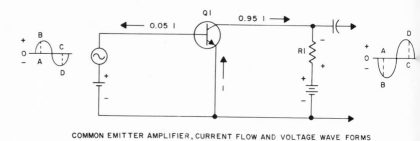

COMMON EMITTER AMPLIFIER, CURRENT FLOW AND VOLTAGE WAVE FORMS

Figure 7

When the positive portion of the input signal aids the forward bias of the transistor, the resultant forward bias is increased. This *increase* in forward bias causes a similar _____ in the total current flow through the emitter.

increase

When the forward bias of an N-P-N common-emitter amplifier is _____ by the positive input signal, both the forward bias and the total emitter current are _____.

aided
increased

When the total emitter current is increased, the collector and base currents are _____.

increased

Increasing the total emitter current flow causes a corresponding increase in the _____ and _____ current flow.

base
collector
(either order)

158

Increasing the collector current flow increases the current flow through resistor R1. The _____ collector current flow through R1 causes the top part of the resistor to become more negative with respect to the bottom part.

⇩

increased

When the flow of collector current is increased, the voltage at the top of resistor R1 becomes more _____ with respect to the bottom point.

⇩

negative

When the voltage at the top of R1 becomes more negative, the output voltage becomes more _____.

⇩

negative

An increase in forward bias causes an increase in total _____ current and in _____ and _____ currents.

⇩

emitter

$\left.\begin{array}{l} base \\ collector \end{array}\right\}$ *(either order)*

An increase in collector current flow causes the voltage at the top of R1 to become more _____ and results in a _____ output voltage.

⇩

negative
negative

The application of a positive input signal to a common-emitter amplifier results in a _____ output signal.

⇩

negative

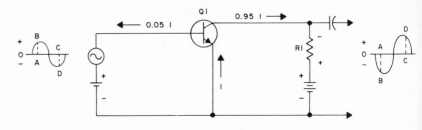

COMMON EMITTER AMPLIFIER, CURRENT FLOW AND VOLTAGE WAVE FORMS

Figure 7

When the negative portion of the input signal (*CD*) reaches the amplifier, it *opposes* the forward bias produced by the base-emitter battery. The forward bias of the amplifier is _____ by the negative ☂ portion of the input signal.

opposed

When the forward bias is opposed by the input signal, the resultant forward bias is decreased. This decrease in forward bias results in a _____ in total ☂ emitter current.

decrease

When the forward bias of an N-P-N common-emitter amplifier is _____ by the negative input signal, both the forward bias and the total emitter ☂ current are _____.

opposed
decreased

When the total emitter current is decreased, the col-
☂ lector and base currents are _____.

decreased

160

Decreasing the total emitter current causes a corresponding decrease in both _____ and
↻ _____ current flow.

Decreasing the collector current flow decreases the current flow through resistor R1. The _____ collector current flow through R1 causes the top part of the resistor to become less negative (or more
↻ _____) with respect to the bottom part.

When the flow of collector _____ is decreased, the top part of R1 will become more _____
↻ with respect to the bottom part.

When the voltage at the top of R1 becomes more positive, the output voltage becomes more
↻ _____.

In an N-P-N common-emitter amplifier, the application of a negative input signal _____ the
↻ forward bias.

A decrease in forward bias causes a decrease in total _____ current and in _____ and
↻ _____ currents.

161

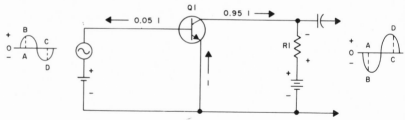

COMMON EMITTER AMPLIFIER, CURRENT FLOW AND VOLTAGE WAVE FORMS

Figure 7

☞ A decrease in collector current flow causes the voltage at the top of R1 to become more _____ and results in a _____ output.

positive
positive

☞ For the entire half cycle that the input signal goes positive, the output signal goes _____.

negative

☞ For the entire half cycle that the input signal goes negative, the output signal goes _____.

positive

☞ What conclusions do you draw from the preceding discussion of phase relationships?

That the input signal voltage is reversed 180° in phase through a common-emitter amplifier.

CURRENT FLOW AND VOLTAGE RELATIONSHIPS; COMMON-COLLECTOR AMPLIFIER

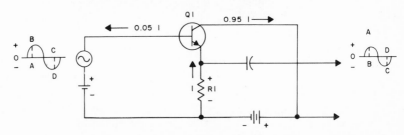

COMMON COLLECTOR AMPLIFIER CURRENT FLOW AND VOLTAGE WAVE FORMS

Figure 8

Figure 8 shows the electron *current* flow through an N-P-N common-collector amplifier. The _____ flow is indicated by the direction of the arrows.

⟡

current

The portions of the emitter current that flow through the _____ and collector are the same as those seen in the common-base amplifier.

⟡

base

When the positive portion of the input signal (*AB*) reaches the amplifier, it *aids* the forward bias. The forward bias of the amplifier is _____ by the positive input signal.

⟡

aided

When the positive input signal aids the forward bias of the amplifier, the resultant bias is increased. This *increase* in forward bias causes a similar _____ in the total current through the emitter.

⟡

increase

When the forward bias of an N-P-N common-collector amplifier is ＿＿＿＿＿＿＿ by the positive input signal, both the forward bias and total emitter current are ＿＿＿＿＿＿＿.

aided
increased

When the total emitter current in the amplifier is increased, the collector and base currents are ＿＿＿＿＿＿＿.

increased

Increasing the total emitter current flow causes a corresponding increase in ＿＿＿＿＿＿＿ and ＿＿＿＿＿＿＿ currents.

base
collector
(either order)

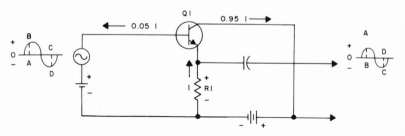

COMMON COLLECTOR AMPLIFIER CURRENT FLOW AND VOLTAGE WAVE FORMS

Figure 8

Increasing the emitter current flow increases the current flow through resistor R1. The ＿＿＿＿＿＿＿ in current flow through R1 causes the top point of the resistor to become more positive with respect to the lower part.

increase

When the flow of emitter current is increased, the top point of R1 becomes more _____ with respect to the lower part.

positive

When the voltage at the top of R1 becomes more positive, the output voltage becomes more _____.

positive

In an N-P-N common-collector amplifier, the application of a positive input signal _____ the forward bias.

increases (aids)

An increase in forward bias causes an increase in total _____ current and in _____ and _____ current.

emitter
base } *(either order)*
collector

An increase in emitter current flow causes the voltage at the top of R1 to become more _____ and results in a _____ output voltage.

positive
positive

The application of a positive input signal to a common-collector amplifier results in a _____ output voltage.

positive

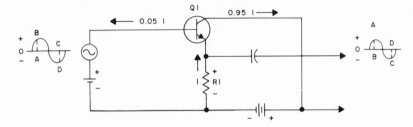

COMMON COLLECTOR AMPLIFIER CURRENT FLOW AND VOLTAGE WAVE FORMS

Figure 8

When the negative portion of the input signal (*CD*) reaches the amplifier, it *opposes* the forward bias. The forward bias is _____ by the negative portion of the input signal.

opposed

When the forward bias is opposed by the input signal, the resultant forward bias is reduced. The *reduction* in forward bias results in a similar _____ in total emitter current.

reduction

When the forward bias of an N-P-N common-collector amplifier is _____ by the negative input signal, both the forward bias and total emitter current are _____.

opposed
reduced

When the total emitter current is reduced, the collector and base currents are _____.

reduced

Reducing the total emitter current causes a corresponding decrease in both _____ and

⬦ _____ currents.

base
collector
(either order)

Decreasing the emitter current *decreases* the current flowing through resistor R1. The _____ current flow through R1 causes the top point of the resistor to become less positive (or more negative)

⬦ with respect to the lower point.

decreased

When the flow of emitter _____ is decreased, the top point of R1 becomes more _____ with

⬦ respect to the lower part.

current
negative

When the voltage at the top of R1 becomes more negative, the output voltage becomes more

⬦ _____.

negative

In an N-P-N common-collector amplifier, the application of a negative input signal _____ the

⬦ forward bias.

reduces (opposes)

A decrease in forward bias causes a decrease in total _____ current and in _____ and

⬦ _____ currents.

emitter

base
collector } *(either order)*

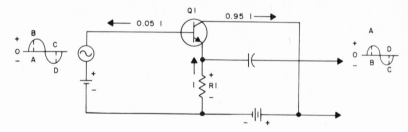

COMMON COLLECTOR AMPLIFIER CURRENT FLOW AND VOLTAGE WAVE FORMS

Figure 8

A decrease in emitter current flow causes the voltage at the top of R1 to become more _____ and results in a _____ output voltage.

negative
negative

For the entire half cycle that the input signal is positive, the output signal is _____.

positive

For the entire half cycle that the input signal is negative, the output signal is _____.

negative

From the preceding discussion, it can be concluded that there _____ (is, is not) a voltage phase reversal of a signal passed through a common-collector amplifier.

is not

Voltage phase reversal is a characteristic of the _____ (Common Base, Common Emitter, Common Collector, or all three) amplifiers.

Common Emitter

In all three amplifier configurations, most of the _____ current flows toward the _____. The approximate percentage is _____.

emitter
collector
95%

168

COMPARISON OF TRANSISTOR
CONFIGURATIONS

ITEM	CB AMPLIFIER	CE AMPLIFIER	CC AMPLIFIER
INPUT RESISTANCE	30 -150 OHMS	500-1,500 OHMS	20K-500K OHMS
OUTPUT RESISTANCE	300K- 500K	30K - 50K	50 -1,000 OHMS
VOLTAGE GAIN	500-1,500	300 -1,000	LESS THAN 1
CURRENT GAIN	LESS THAN 1	25 - 50	25 - 50
POWER GAIN	20 - 30 DB	25 - 40 DB	10 - 20 DB

Table 1

Having considered the three types of transistor configurations, we can compare their properties as amplifiers. For this comparison refer to Table 1. Table 1
lists typical values of input resistances, output resistances, current gain, voltage gain, and power gain for
the three configurations.

⊽ *Proceed to the next frame.*

Voltage gain or (A_v) is the *ratio* of the signal output
voltage to the signal input voltage. A_v is the
_____ of the signal output voltage (E_{out})
⊽ to the signal input voltage (E_{in}).

ratio

The voltage gain of a transistor is:
⊽
$$A_v = \underline{\hspace{3cm}}.$$

$A_v = \dfrac{E_{out}}{E_{in}}$

Current gain or (A_i) is the ratio of the signal *output*
current to the signal *input* current. A_i is the ratio of
the signal _____ current (I_{out}) to the signal
⊽ _____ current (I_{in}).

output
input

The current gain of a transistor is:

⌄ $A_i = $ _____.

$$A_i = \frac{I_{out}}{I_{in}}$$

Power gain or (G) is the ratio of the *output* signal power (P_{out}) to the input signal power (P_{in}) expressed in *db*. G is the ratio of the _____ signal power to the input signal power expressed in

⌄   _____.

output
db

The power gain of a transistor is:

⌄ $G = $ _____.

$$G = \frac{P_{out}}{P_{in}} db$$

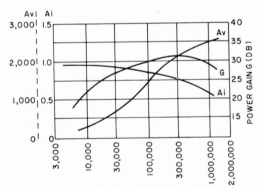

Av = VOLTAGE AMPLIFICATION
Ai = CURRENT AMPLIFICATION

COMMON-BASE, VOLTAGE, CURRENT, AND
POWER GAIN CHARACTERISTIC CURVES

Figure 11

Figure 11 shows the comparison of the various gains of a common-base amplifier.

⌄   *Proceed to next frame.*

170

The current gain, the voltage gain, and the power gain are plotted against the *load* resistance. The values of _____ resistance are plotted on the abscissa.

▽ *load*

The _____ gain (A_i) is always less than one and decreases as the load resistance is increased.

▽ *current*

Increasing the load resistance in a common-base amplifier causes the A_i to _____.

▽ *decrease*

The current gain of a common-base amplifier is never more than _____.

▽ *one (unity)*

The voltage gain increases as the load resistance is increased. An increase in load resistance will cause the A_v to _____.

▽ *increase*

The maximum power gain (G) for this particular transistor occurs when the load resistance is approximately 300,000 ohms. The power gain _____ (is, is not) at its maximum when the load resistance is 300,000 ohms.

▽ *is*

In a common-base amplifier, as the load resistance is increased, the _____ $(A_v, A_i, G,$ all three) is always less than one and decreases.

▽ A_i

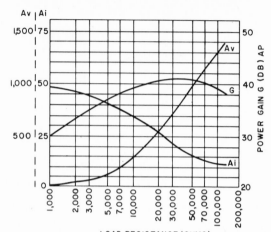

Av = VOLTAGE AMPLIFICATION
Ai = CURRENT AMPLIFICATION
G = POWER GAIN

COMMON-EMITTER, VOLTAGE, CURRENT, AND
POWER GAIN CHARACTERISTIC CURVES

Figure 12

Figure 12 shows the comparison of the various gains of a common-emitter amplifier.

▽ *Proceed to next frame.*

The _____ gain (A_i) decreases as the load resistance increases. If the load resistance decreases,
▽ the current gain will _____.

current
increase

The voltage gain (A_v) increases as the load resistance is increased. A_v varies directly as the _____
▽ resistance.

load

The maximum power gain (G) occurs when the load resistance is approximately 40,000 ohms. If the load resistance is decreased below 40,000 ohms, the G will
▽ also _____.

decrease

172

In Figure 12, the current, voltage, and power gains

⟱ _____ (may, may not) exceed unity.

may

In a common-emitter amplifier, Figure 12,
_____ (A_i, A_v, G) shows the most gain as

⟱ the load resistance is increased.

A_v

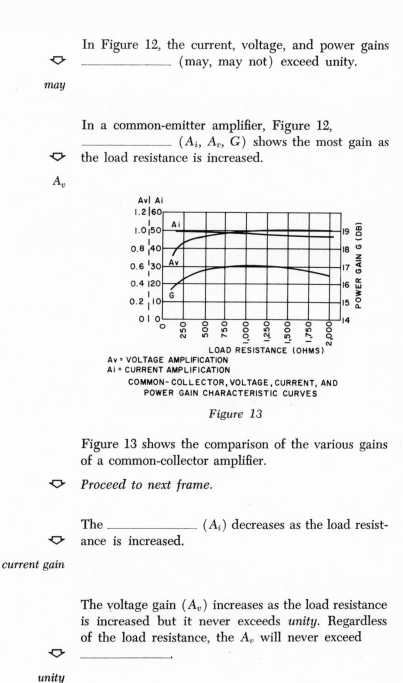

Av = VOLTAGE AMPLIFICATION
Ai = CURRENT AMPLIFICATION
COMMON- COLLECTOR, VOLTAGE, CURRENT, AND
POWER GAIN CHARACTERISTIC CURVES

Figure 13

Figure 13 shows the comparison of the various gains
of a common-collector amplifier.

⟱ *Proceed to next frame.*

The _____ (A_i) decreases as the load resist-

⟱ ance is increased.

current gain

The voltage gain (A_v) increases as the load resistance
is increased but it never exceeds *unity*. Regardless
of the load resistance, the A_v will never exceed

⟱ _____ .

unity

173

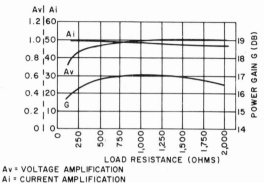

AV = VOLTAGE AMPLIFICATION
AI = CURRENT AMPLIFICATION
COMMON-COLLECTOR, VOLTAGE, CURRENT, AND
POWER GAIN CHARACTERISTIC CURVES

Figure 13

The maximum power gain (G) occurs when the load resistance is approximately 1000 ohms. If the load resistance is 1500 ohms, the power gain _____ (is, is not) at maximum.

is not

In a common-collector amplifier _____ (A_i, A_v, G, all three) can never exceed unity.

A_v

In a common-base amplifier, the current gain never exceeds _____ .

unity

In a _____ - _____ amplifier, the current, voltage, and power gains all may exceed unity.

common-emitter

174

ITEM	CB AMPLIFIER	CE AMPLIFIER	CC AMPLIFIER
INPUT RESISTANCE	30-150 OHMS	500-1,500 OHMS	20K-500K OHMS
OUTPUT RESISTANCE	300K-500K	30K-50K	50-1,000 OHMS
VOLTAGE GAIN	500-1,500	300-1,000	LESS THAN I
CURRENT GAIN	LESS THAN I	25-50	25-50
POWER GAIN	20-30 DB	25-40 DB	10-20 DB

Table 1

Table 1 is a comparison of input resistance, output resistance, A_v, A_i, and G for the common-base, common-emitter, and common-collector amplifiers.

▽ *Proceed to next frame.*

Since the output of most electronic circuits is converted to some form of work, the power gain is a basic criterion. From Table 1, we see that the

_____-_____ amplifier has the largest power gain
▽ of the three configurations.

common-emitter

Of the three amplifiers, the common-emitter has the
▽ _____ power gain.

largest

Because of its large _____ gain, the common-emitter amplifier is the most used type for transistor
▽ amplifiers.

power

Table 1 shows that the common-base amplifier has a sizable power gain, but it is considerably
▽ _____ than that of the common-emitter.

less

175

ITEM	CB AMPLIFIER	CE AMPLIFIER	CC AMPLIFIER
INPUT RESISTANCE	30-150 OHMS	500-1,500 OHMS	20K-500K OHMS
OUTPUT RESISTANCE	300K-500K	30K-50K	50-1,000 OHMS
VOLTAGE GAIN	500-1,500	300-1,000	LESS THAN 1
CURRENT GAIN	LESS THAN 1	25-50	25-50
POWER GAIN	20-30 DB	25-40 DB	10-20 DB

Table 1

If a large power output were desired from a transistor amplifier, the _____ (CB, CE, CC) configuration would be the most logical choice.

▽

CE

Table 1 shows that the voltage gain of the _____-_____ amplifier is the greatest of all three configurations.

▽

common-base

If an application requires only a voltage output, the _____-_____ is the best configuration.

▽

common-base

Table 1 shows that the voltage and power gains for the common-collector amplifier are low. The current gain, however, is _____.

▽

high

For use in voltage or power amplification circuits, the common-collector amplifier _____ (would, would not) be a logical choice.

▽

would not

The input resistance of a *common-base* amplifier is shown to be much lower than the output resistance. As a result the _____-_____ amplifier can be used to match a low impedance circuit to a high impedance circuit.

▽

common-base

176

The common-base amplifier would be the best configuration for matching a _____ impedance
to a _____ impedance.

low
high

For the common-collector amplifier, Table 1 shows that
the input resistance is much higher than the output
resistance. For this reason, the common-_____
amplifier is most commonly used to match a high impedance circuit to a low impedance circuit.

collector

The _____ (CB, CE, CC) amplifier is most
often used to match a high impedance circuit to a low
impedance circuit.

CC

In summary then, the common-_____ is the
best power amplifier, the common-_____ is
the best voltage amplifier, and the common-
_____ is most often used as an impedance
matching circuit.

emitter
base
collector

177

set **10** **BASE LEAD CURRENT**

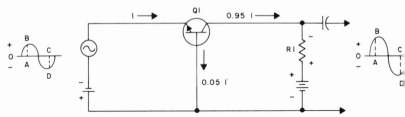

COMMON BASE AMPLIFIER, CURRENT FLOW AND VOLTAGE WAVE FORMS

Figure 6

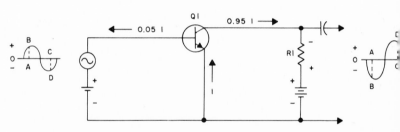

COMMON EMITTER AMPLIFIER, CURRENT FLOW AND VOLTAGE WAVE FORMS

Figure 7

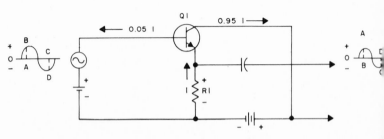

COMMON COLLECTOR AMPLIFIER CURRENT FLOW AND VOLTAGE WAVE FORMS

Figure 8

178

Figures 6, 7, and 8 show the electron current in the base lead of the N-P-N transistor to be flowing away from the base region but ignoring the reverse bias current flow between the collector and base.

For a P-N-P transistor, the electron current flow in the base lead would be toward the base region at all times if the reverse bias collector base current were to be ignored.

For either type of transistor, the direction of current flow in the base region depends on the percentage of emitter current and the magnitude of the reverse-bias collector base current entering the base lead.

⇨ *Proceed to next frame.*

Figures 6, 7, and 8 ignore the reverse-bias current flow between the ______________ and ______________. ⇨

collector
base

If the reverse-bias current flow between collector and base in an N-P-N transistor were ignored, the base lead current would flow ______________ (away from, toward) the base region. ⇨

away from

If the reverse-bias current flow between collector and base in a P-N-P transistor were ignored, the base lead current would flow ______________ (away from, toward) the base region. ⇨

toward

Ignoring the reverse-bias collector-base current flow, the base lead current in an N-P-N transistor would flow ______________ (away from, toward) the base region, and in a P-N-P transistor, ______________ (away from, toward) the base region. ⇨

away from
toward

The direction of the base region current is determined by the percentage of emitter current and magnitude of reverse-bias _____ - _____ current

⇩ entering the base lead.

collector-base

The percentage of emitter current and the magnitude of reverse-bias collector-base current determine the direction of current flow in the _____ lead

⇩ of an N-P-N or a P-N-P transistor.

base

In order to fully understand how the base lead current is affected by the emitter current and reverse-bias current, a knowledge of certain definitions and symbols is necessary. Do you think that symbols are

⇩ important in a technical subject?

They sure are! They serve as a convenient shorthand for representing physical quantities.

The *current gain* of a CB amplifier is the ratio of the collector current to the emitter current. In a CB amplifier the value of the collector current divided by the value of the emitter current is the _____

⇩ _____.

current gain

⇩ The current gain of a CB amplifier is the ratio of the collector current to the _____ current.

emitter

We use the symbol "α_{fb}" to represent the current gain of a CB amplifier. "α_{fb}" equals the _____

⇩ current divided by the _____ current.

collector

emitter

180

The current gain of a CB amplifier is represented
by ⸺⸺⸺⸺ (symbol).

"α_{fb}"

In a CB amplifier, the emitter current is ten amps.
and the collector current is five amps.
(1) $\alpha_{fb} =$ ⸺⸺⸺⸺ (calculate answer).
(2) The current gain of this circuit is ⸺⸺⸺⸺.

½ (or 0.5)
½ (or 0.5)

The subscript "f" of α_{fb} is the current from the emitter
to the collector, that is, in a ⸺orward direction.

forward

Current flow in a forward direction is indicated by
the subscript letter ⸺ in the symbol for current
gain.

f

The subscript "b" in the symbol α_{fb} indicates that a
common-⸺ase amplifier is being used.

base

The letters "f" and "b" in the symbol α_{fb} indicate
⸺⸺⸺⸺ current and that a ⸺⸺⸺⸺-
⸺⸺⸺⸺ amplifier is used.

forward
common-base

Roughly, α_{fb} represents the percentage of emitter current that reaches the collector. The percentage of
emitter current reaching the collector can be designated as ⸺⸺⸺⸺ (give symbol).

α_{fb}

181

The total emitter current is designated I_e.

⊽ _____ is the symbol for total _____ current.

I_e
emitter

The *reverse-bias current* flow between base and collector is designated I_{CBO}. The symbol I_{CBO} designates

⊽ the _____ - _____ flow between base and collector.

reverse-bias current

The subscripts "C" and "B" of the symbol I_{CBO} indicate that a ____ollector-____ase current is being meas-

⊽ ured.

collector-base

The subscript "O" of the symbol I_{CBO} indicates that collector-base current is being measured with the

⊽ emitter ____pen.

open

To measure collector-base current the emitter is

⊽ _____.

open

The reverse-bias current flow is designated

⊽ _____ (give symbol).

I_{CBO}

The total emitter current is designated by

⊽ _____ (give symbol).

I_e

The current gain of a CB amplifier is designated

⊽ _____ (give symbol).

α_{fb}

182

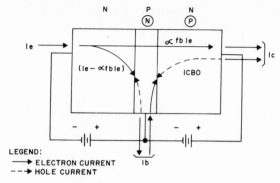

CURRENT FLOW IN AN NPN TRANSISTOR

Figure 9

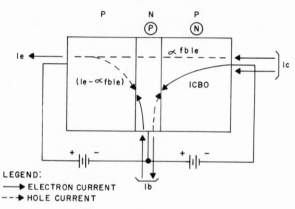

CURRENT FLOW IN A PNP TRANSISTOR

Figure 10

Panel 2

Figure 9 shows an N-P-N transistor with the proper biases applied. The following discussion applies also to the P-N-P transistor. Internally, however, the electron and hole currents are interchanged. Externally, the polarity of the biases and the direction of electron current flow are reversed.

Refer to Panel 2. To the minority carriers, *electrons*, in the base region, the base region acts as N-type germanium. This is indicated by the circled N (Figure 9). _____ are the minority carriers in the base region.

Electrons

183

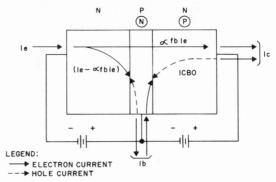

CURRENT FLOW IN AN NPN TRANSISTOR

Figure 9

The base region acts as N-type germanium to the minority carriers. This is indicated by the circled

⬙ _____.

N

To the minority carriers, *holes,* in the collector region, the collector region acts as P-type germanium. This is indicated by the circled P (Figure 9).

⬙ _____ are the minority carriers in the collector region.

Holes

The collector region acts as P-type germanium to the

⬙ _____ in the collector region.

holes

Panel 3

The emitter current (I_e) consists of electrons (majority carriers); 92 to 99 percent of the electrons $(\alpha_{fb}I_e)$ go through the base region and collector region into the positive terminal of the collector-base battery. About 1 to 8 percent of the emitter electrons $(I_e - \alpha_{fb}I_e)$ combine in the base-emitter junction with holes from the base region.

184

Refer to Panel 3. The positive terminal of the collector-base battery collects from ____________ to ____________ percent of the emitter electrons.

92 to 99

The symbol $\alpha_{fb}I_e$ indicates the percentage of ____________ electrons that flow to the collector-base battery.

emitter

α_{fb} multiplied by I_e or $\alpha_{fb}I_e$ designates current gain times total ____________.

emitter current

About 1 to 8 percent of the electrons from the emitter are combined with holes from the base region in the ______-______ junction.

base-emitter

The base-emitter junction is the point where approximately ____________ to ____________ percent of the emitter electrons are combined with holes from the base.

1 to 8

The symbol $(I_e - \alpha_{fb}I_e)$ indicates the total ____________ minus the current that flows to the collector.

emitter current

Of the total emitter current electrons, about 92 to 99 percent, $\alpha_{fb}I_e$, flow to the positive terminal of the ______-______ battery and about 1 to 8 percent combine with ____________ at the base-emitter junction.

collector-base
holes

The holes which combine with the emitter electrons are *generated* in the base region near the base lead. Holes are _____ in the base region near the

⇩ base lead.

generated

Generation of the holes causes an electron current to flow in the base lead and *away* from the base. Current flow in the base lead caused by generation of the holes in the base region flows _____ from

⇩ the base.

away

Current flow in the base lead which flows away from the base is caused by the generation of _____

⇩ in the base region.

holes

Panel 4

Reverse-bias current (I_{CBO}) flows between the base and the collector. I_{CBO} consists of a flow of electrons in the base region that combine with holes from the collector region at the base collector junction.

Electrons from the base region combine with holes from the collector region and form _____ -

⇩ current (I_{CBO}).

reverse-bias

I_{CBO} is a result of base electrons combining with col-

⇩ lector holes at the _____ - _____ junction.

base-collector

The reverse-bias current causes a flow of electrons in the base lead toward the base. I_{CBO} causes the cur-

⇩ rent in the base lead to flow _____ the base.

toward

186

Generation of holes in the base region causes base
lead current to flow _____ the base and
I_{CBO} causes the base lead current to flow
▽   _____ the base.

away from
toward

The direction of the current flow in the base lead
depends on the relative magnitude of $I_c - \alpha_{fb}I_e$ and
I_{CBO}. The relative magnitudes of _____ and
_____ determine the direction of base lead
▽   current flow (use symbols).

$I_e - \alpha_{fb}I_e$
I_{CBO}

If the emitter-base current $(I_e - \alpha_{fb}I_e)$ is larger than
I_{CBO}, base lead current flows away from the base region. If $I_e - \alpha_{fb}I_e$ is less than I_{CBO}, base lead current
flows toward the base region.

▽   *Proceed to next frame.*

For clarification, study the following example.

Example 1

Given: $I_e = 1$ ma
                      $I_{CBO} = 0.01$ ma
                      $\alpha_{fb} = 0.92$

Determine the emitter-base current.

$I_c - \alpha_{fb}I_e = 1 - 0.92 \times 1$
▽ $= $ _____ ma

0.08 ma

In Example 1, the emitter-base current (0.08 ma) is
larger than the I_{CBO} and therefore the base lead current is flowing _____ (toward, away from)
▽   the base region.

away from

187

Example 2

Given:
$$I_e = 1 \text{ ma}$$
$$I_{CBO} = 0.02 \text{ ma}$$
$$\alpha_{fb} = 0.99$$

Determine the emitter-base current

$$I_e - \alpha_{fb}I_e = 1 - 0.99 \times 1$$
$$= \underline{\hspace{2cm}} \text{ ma}$$

⇩

0.01 ma

In example 2, the emitter-base current (0.01 ma) is smaller than I_{CBO} (0.02 ma) and therefore the base lead current is flowing _____ (toward, away from) the base region.

⇩

toward

When I_{CBO} is smaller than $I_e - \alpha_{fb}I_e$, the base lead current flows _____ the base.

⇩

away from

When I_{CBO} is greater than $I_e - \alpha_{fb}I_e$, the base lead current flows _____ base.

⇩

toward the

The percentage of emitter current electrons that reach the collector-base battery is approximately _____ to _____ percent.

⇩

92 to 99

_____ to _____ percent of the emitter current electrons reach the base.

⇩

1 to 8

Give the symbols for the following:

(1) Current gain of a CB amplifier _____.

(2) Total emitter current _____.

(3) Total emitter current reaching collector-base battery _____.

(4) Reverse-bias current _____.

⬇ (5) Emitter-base current _____.

(1) α_{fb}

(2) I_e

(3) $\alpha_{fb}I_e$

(4) I_{CBO}

(5) $I_e - \alpha_{fb}I_c$

PART FOUR

OSCILLATION

REVIEW OF CIRCUIT
CONFIGURATION CHARACTERISTICS

A common-base circuit configuration has an output current which is *less than* ($<$) the input current. This means that the current gain (A_i) for a common-base circuit configuration is _____ one.

less than ($<$)

If we had a common-base configuration circuit with an input current of 1 microamp we would know that the output current would be _____ 1 microamp.

less than ($<$)

The current gain (A_i) for the _____ - _____ configuration is less than ($<$) _____.

common-base
one

There is no phase reversal ($0°$) between input and output terminals of the common-base configuration. The input and output terminals of the common-base configuration are _____ (in, out of) phase.

in

In the common-base configuration, there _____ (is, is no) phase reversal.

is no ($0°$ phase)

The difference in phase between the input and output terminals of the common base is _____ ($0°$, $180°$).

$0°$

193

Give two characteristics of the common-base configuration.

▽ (1) _____. (2) _____.

▽

(1) The current gain for the common-base configuration is less than one.
(2) There is no phase reversal (0°) between the input and output terminals.

Voltage gain (A_v) and power gain (G) for the common base are greater than one.

A_v _____ (=, <, >) one.
G _____ (=, <, >) one.

▽

>
>

For the common base:

A_v _____ (=, <, >) one.
G _____ (=, <, >) one.

▽

>
>

The common-base configuration has the following characteristics: _____ phase reversal; voltage and power gains _____ one; _____ input impedance and high output impedance; current gain _____ than one.

▽

no (0°)
greater than (>)
low
less

194

The common-base configuration has

A_i (current gain) ______________ (<, >) 1

A_v (voltage gain) ______________ (<, >) 1

Input impedance is ______________ (<, >) output impedance, G (gain) ______________ (<, >) 1

(Use symbols.)

<

>

<

>

Is a phase reversal a characteristic of the common-base configuration? ______________.

No. It is 0°.

The common emitter has moderate input and output impedances; no matching in the feedback circuits is necessary. Since the common emitter has moderate input and output impedance, no ______________ in the feedback circuit is necessary.

matching

No ______________ between input and output impedances is necessary in the common-emitter configuration.

matching

Impedance matching in the ______-______ configuration is not necessary because it has ______________ input and output impedances.

common-emitter
moderate

In the common-emitter circuit, there is a *phase reversal (180°)* between input and output. The input is
_____° out of phase with the output in a
common-emitter circuit.

↧

180°

The common-emitter circuit exhibits a _____
(180°) between input and output.

↧

phase reversal

What circuit exhibits a 180° phase reversal between
the input and output? _____.

↧

*You're right (assuming
you said common-emitter).*

The current, voltage, and power gains are *all greater
than* one for the common emitter. The common
emitter has current, voltage, and power gains all
_____ one.

↧

greater than (>)

The common-emitter configuration exhibits the following characteristics:

A_i _____ (=, <, >) one
A_v _____ (=, <, >) one
G _____ (=, <, >) one

↧

>
>
>

196

The common emitter exhibits the following characteristics: there _____ (is, is not) a phase reversal (180°) between input and output; current, voltage, and power gains are _____ than one; no impedance _____ is needed because

of the moderate input and output impedances.

is
greater
matching

The common-collector configuration has high input and moderate output impedances necessitating *matching* in the feedback circuit. M_____ in the feedback circuit is needed when the common-collector configuration is used because of the high input and moderate output impedances.

Matching

In the common-collector configuration, _____ of the input and output impedance is necessary.

matching

The common collector has *no phase reversal (0°)* between input and output. The input and output of a common collector are _____ (in, out of) phase.

in

For the common collector, there _____ (is, is no) phase reversal (____°) between input and output.

is no
0°

197

Is the following statement true or false? Both the common-base and common-collector configurations have no phase reversal. _____.

true

The common collector has current and power gains *greater than* one. The current and power gains for the common collector are _____ _____ one.

greater than ($>$)

The common collector exhibits the following:

$$A_i \text{_____} (=, <, >) \text{ one}$$
$$G \text{_____} (=, <, >) \text{ one}$$

$>$
$>$

The common collector has a voltage gain less than one. The voltage gain for the common collector is _____ ($=, <, >$) one.

$<$

The common _____ and common _____ have no phase reversal between input and output.

base
collector
(either order)

The common _____ has a phase reversal (180°) between the input and output.

emitter

198

The common collector exhibits the following: because of the high input and moderate output impedances a _____ network of the input and output should be used; voltage gain is _____ than one; current and power gains are _____ than one; _____ phase reversal exists between input and output.

↻

matching
less
greater
no (0°)

The transistor configurations which require a matching network in the feedback circuit are the common _____ and common _____ circuits.

↻

base
collector
(either order)

The only configuration which has current, voltage, and power gains greater than one is the common _____.

↻

emitter

Do you feel that you know the following characteristics A_i, A_v, G, phase relationships, and matching are associated with the common-base, common-collector, and common-emitter configurations?

↻

If your answer was yes, proceed to the next set. If your answer was no or maybe, review this set.

set *2* # CHARACTERISTICS OF THE
TRANSISTOR OSCILLATOR

An oscillator is an electronic device which generates AC current from a DC source. An electronic device which generates AC current from a DC source is called an _____.

▽

oscillator

▽ An electronic device which generates _____ current from a DC source is an oscillator.

AC

▽ The function of an oscillator is _____.

to generate AC current from a DC source

An oscillator which operates with the application of a supply voltage is said to be *self-excited*. A _____ - oscillator is one which oscillates when a supply voltage is introduced.

▽

self-excited

One major type of oscillator requiring only a supply voltage for operation is a _____ - _____ oscillator.

▽

self-excited

A self-excited oscillator requires only a _____ _____ for operation.

▽

supply voltage

200

An oscillator requiring an external triggering signal in order to oscillate is an *externally triggered* oscillator. _____ oscillators require external triggering signals for operation.

⊽

Externally triggered

The two main types of oscillators are the self-excited and the _____.

⊽

externally triggered

An externally triggered oscillator requires an _____ in order to oscillate.

⊽

external trigger

Name the two major types of oscillators.
(1) _____ (2) _____

⊽

self-excited
externally triggered
(either order)

Oscillators are electronic devices which generate _____ current from a _____ source. Both the _____ and _____ oscillators perform this function.

⊽

AC
DC

self-excited⎫
externally ⎬*(either order)*
triggered⎭

The three requirements for a transistor oscillator are *frequency determining elements, proper DC bias voltages,* and *regenerative* (positive) feedback. Frequency determining elements, proper DC biasing voltages, and r_____ feedback are necessary for transistor oscillators.

⊽

regenerative

201

Transistor oscillators require regenerative feedback, proper -_____ and frequency determining elements to operate.

⟁

d-c biasing

Regenerative feedback, _____ determining elements, and proper d-c biasing are required for transistor oscillators.

⟁

frequency

Name the three requirements necessary for transistor oscillators.

(1) _____   (2) _____

⟁   (3) _____

DC biasing voltages
frequency determining
elements
regenerative or positive
feedback
　　　　(any order)

Frequency determining elements consist of *LC* networks, *RC* networks, or crystals. *LC* networks, _____ networks, and crystals are the frequency determining elements.

⟁

RC

Frequency determining elements consist of *LC* networks, *RC* networks, and _____ .

⟁

crystals

The three frequency determining elements are RC networks, _____ networks, and crystals.

⟁

LC

How many different type *networks* are used as frequency determining elements in an oscillator (a crystal is not a *network*) _____.

Name them: _____ network, _____

⇩ network

2

$LC \brace RC$ *(either order)*

Name the three frequency determining elements.

(1) _____ (2) _____

⇩ (3) _____

RC networks
LC networks
crystals

Poor *bias stabilization* adversely affects the output amplitude, waveform, and frequency stability. The output amplitude, waveform, and frequency are adversely affected by poor b_____ s_____ .

⇩

bias stabilization

Poor bias stabilization adversely affects the output amplitude, waveform, and f_____y.

⇩

frequency

The output amplitude, _____, and frequency are affected by poor bias stabilization.

⇩

waveform

Poor bias stabilization affects the output _____, waveform, and frequency.

⇩

amplitude

203

Poor bias stabilization affects the output _____, _____, and _____.

⟱ How important is good DC bias stabilization?

What are the three types of frequency determining elements?

(1) _____   (2) _____

⟱ (3) _____

Regenerative or positive feedback is the portion of the output wave that is returned *in phase* with the input wave. The portion of the output wave that is fed back _____ phase with the input is called regen-

⟱ erative feedback.

R_____ feedback is that portion of the output

⟱ that is fed back in phase with the input.

The principal factor in regenerative feedback is that the feedback wave be _____ with the input

⟱ wave.

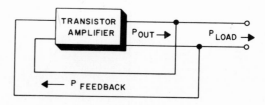

TRANSISTOR OSCILLATOR SHOWING APPLICATION
OF FEEDBACK, BLOCK DIAGRAM

Figure 1

In Figure 1, the power delivered to the load is $P_{\text{out}} - P_{\text{feedback}}$. The $P_{\text{out}} - P$ _____ is the power delivered to the load.

⇩

P_{feedback}

The power delivered to the load is equal to the

⇩

_____ $-$ _____.

$P_{\text{out}} - P_{\text{feedback}}$

If the gain (G) of an amplifier is $<$ (less than) *one*, a damped oscillation will be obtained. For damped oscillations, $G <$ _____.

⇩

one

Damped oscillations occur in an oscillator circuit when G is _____ ($<$, $>$, or $=$) one.

⇩

$<$ *(less than)*

To sustain oscillations, the gain (G) must be equal to or greater than $(\geqq)$ *one*. If $G \geqq$ _____, oscillations will be sustained.

⇩

one

For an oscillator to sustain oscillations, G must be _____ ($\leqq$, $\geqq$, $<$) one.

⇩

$\geqq$ *(equal to or greater than)*

205

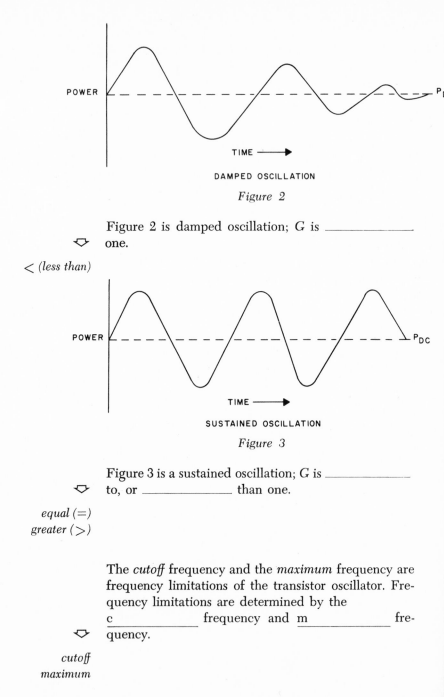

DAMPED OSCILLATION

Figure 2

Figure 2 is damped oscillation; G is _____
one.

< *(less than)*

SUSTAINED OSCILLATION

Figure 3

Figure 3 is a sustained oscillation; G is _____
to, or _____ than one.

equal (=)
greater (>)

The *cutoff* frequency and the *maximum* frequency are
frequency limitations of the transistor oscillator. Frequency limitations are determined by the
c _____ frequency and m _____ frequency.

cutoff
maximum

206

The cutoff frequency of a transistor is f_a.

⇩ _____ is called the cutoff frequency of a transistor.

f_a

⇩ f_a is the symbol for the _____ frequency of a transistor.

cutoff

The cutoff frequency is usually related to the current gain and is determined by using the *common-emitter* or *common-base* configuration. The common

e _____ and common-b _____ circuits

⇩ are used in determining the cutoff frequency.

emitter
base

The cutoff frequency for the common-emitter amplifier is f_{ac}. _____ is the cutoff frequency

⇩ for the common-emitter transistor.

f_{ae}

The cutoff frequency for the common-*base* amplifier is f_{ab}. _____ is the cutoff frequency for the

⇩ common-base transistor.

f_{ab}

The cutoff frequency is the point at which the *current gain* drops 3 db or .707 of its low frequency value. If the current drops _____ db or .707 times its low frequency checkpoint value, the cutoff frequency of

⇩ the transistor is determined.

3db

A loss of _____ db in the current gain from its
↶ low frequency checkpoint value determines f_a.

3db

f_a is the point at which the _____ gain drops
↶ 3 db from its low frequency checkpoint value.

current

The cutoff frequency for a common-base amplifier,
f_{ab}, is the frequency at which the _____
_____ is 3 db below the low checkpoint
↶ frequency value.

current gain

The normal low frequency checkpoint of a transistor
is *1000* cps. _____ cps is the normal low
↶ frequency checkpoint of a transistor.

1000

The cutoff frequency of a common-emitter amplifier,
f_{ae}, is the frequency at which the current gain is 3 db
↶ down from the gain at _____ cps.

1000

An oscillator can operate above cutoff frequency and
up to, but not above, the *maximum frequency* f_{max}.
↶ Oscillators cannot operate above _____.

maximum frequency (f_{max})

An oscillator can operate above f_a but cannot operate
↶ above _____.

f_{max}

f_{max} is the frequency at which the power gain of the transistor is *unity*. The power gain at f_{max} is equal to

⬦ _____.

unity (1)

Theoretically, an oscillator could be constructed with the power gain at f_{max} equal to one, but due to the losses in the feedback circuit, oscillations will not be sustained.

⬦ *Proceed to the next frame.*

Since there are losses in the feedback circuit, the transistor oscillator cannot operate at f_{max}. Operation of a transistor at f_{max} is _____ (possible, not possible) because there are _____ (no losses, losses) in the feedback circuit.

⬦

not possible
losses

An operating frequency *below* f_{max} is required to sustain transistor oscillations. Transistor oscillator circuits operate only at frequencies _____ f_{max}.

⬦

below

Transistor oscillators may operate above _____ (f_a, f_{max}) but cannot operate at _____ (f_a, f_{max}).

⬦

f_a
f_{max}

The *common-base* configuration has the lowest input and highest output impedances. The c_____- b_____ configuration has the _____ output impedance and the _____ input impedance.

⬦

common-base
highest
lowest

The low input impedance and the _____ output impedance are characteristics of the common-base configuration.

↻

high

Give two characteristics of the common-base configuration.

↻ (1) _____ (2) _____

low input impedance
high output impedance

Because the common base has the lowest input and highest output impedance, *matching* of the output to the input through the feedback network must be made. The feedback network must m_____ the output to the input in the common-base configuration.

↻

match

In the common-base configuration, compensation for the _____ in the feedback network or _____ of the unequal impedances must be made.

↻

losses
matching

FEEDBACK IN
TRANSISTOR OSCILLATORS

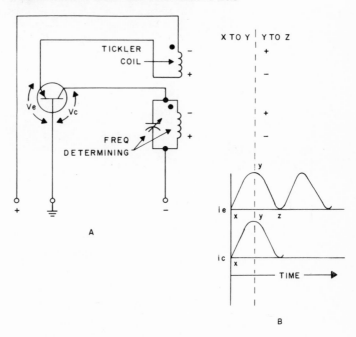

TYPICAL TRANSISTOR OSCILLATOR AND CURRENT WAVEFORMS

Figure 4

Regenerative feedback in the self-excited oscillator in Figure 4 is coupled from the collector to the emitter by a *tickler coil*. A _____ is used to couple feedback from the collector to the emitter in the self-excited oscillator.

☞ *tickler coil*

The coupling of feedback from the collector to the emitter in the self-excited oscillator is accomplished by use of a _____.

☞ *tickler coil*

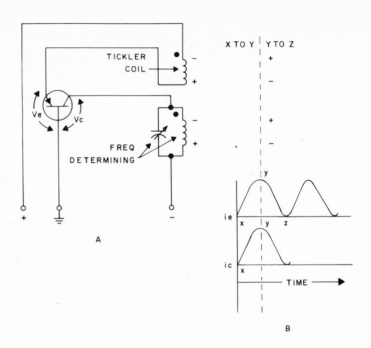

TYPICAL TRANSISTOR OSCILLATOR AND CURRENT WAVEFORMS

Figure 4

The _____ to _____ feedback in the self-excited oscillator is coupled by use of a tickler coil.

⟡

collector to emitter

Regenerative _____, in the self-excited oscillator in Figure 4 is coupled from the collector to the _____ by a _____

⟡ _____.

feedback
emitter
tickler coil

Due to regenerative feedback in the self-excited oscillator, the current flow in the circuit will steadily *increase*. The current flow in the circuit will steadily ⟡ _____ due to the regenerative feedback.

increase

The steadily increasing current flow in the oscillator circuit is caused by the _____ feedback.

regenerative

The current steadily increases in the oscillator circuit until a point (point Y in Figure 4b) is reached where the *collector current* can no longer increase. At this point, the transistor is said to be *saturated*.

Proceed to the next frame.

The _____ point of a transistor is reached when the collector current (i_c) can no longer be increased.

saturation

The steadily increasing collector current (i_c) will drive the transistor into _____.

saturation

A transistor is said to be at saturation when its _____ current can no longer be increased.

collector

When is a transistor saturated?

when its collector current can no longer increase

When saturation is reached, collector current stops increasing. At this instant we have no induction of current into the tickler coil; therefore feedback has ceased and the emitter current begins to decrease. As a result of this, the collector current begins to decrease causing induction of current in the tickler coil but in the opposite direction. This causes emitter current to decrease further, decreasing the collector current even more.

Proceed to next frame.

213

When the transistor is saturated, no further increase in collector current takes place and feedback ⧄ _____ (ceases, begins).

ceases

Feedback _____ when the transistor reaches ⧄ _____ .

ceases
saturation

When the transistor reaches its saturation point, feedback from the collector to the emitter ceases and emitter current (i_e) begins to _____ (decrease, increase). ⧄

decrease

The decrease in emitter current (I_e) is a direct result of the _____ (absence, presence) of feedback. ⧄

absence

As a result of feedback ceasing, emitter current begins to decrease causing collector current (I_c) to ⧄ _____ (increase, decrease).

decrease

The _____ (decrease, increase) in emitter current results in a decrease in collector current causing a feedback to be induced into the tickler coil, which is now opposite in polarity to what we had ⧄ before.

decrease

214

The decrease in collector current causes a negative going or inverse feedback and the emitter current

⇩ _____ (decreases, increases) even more.

decreases

_____ starts again when the decrease in emitter current (I_e) causes a decrease in collector current (I_c), and therefore, induction of voltage into

⇩ the tickler coil.

Feedback

The inverse feedback causes a steady _____

⇩ in emitter current.

decrease

The decrease in _____ current, which is caused by the inverse feedback, causes a decrease in _____ current which results in a

⇩ _____ (greater, smaller) inverse feedback.

emitter
collector
greater

The steadily decreasing _____ (I_e) current

⇩ is due to the inverse feedback.

emitter

The _____ feedback from the collector to

⇩ the emitter causes the emitter current to decrease.

inverse

The decreasing emitter current, which causes a decrease in collector current, is due to the _____

⇩ feedback.

inverse

215

The emitter current decreases, due to inverse feedback, causing collector current to decrease giving more inverse feedback. This condition continues until cutoff is reached. The emitter current _____ until cutoff is reached.

▽

decreases

The emitter current _____ (increases, decreases, remains the same) causing collector current to _____ (remain the same, increase, decrease) until cutoff is reached.

▽

decreases
decrease

The inverse feedback will continue until the _____ is cut off.

▽

transistor
or
oscillator

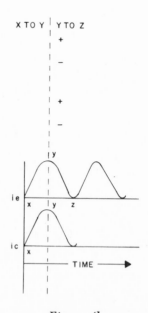

Figure 4b

The emitter current _____ until cutoff is reached. This cutoff point is represented by point

⌄   Z of Figure 4b.

decreases

When the emitter current reaches point Z, the tran-

⌄   sistor is said to be _____.

cut off

When emitter current can no longer decrease, the transistor has reached _____, and the emitter-

⌄   base diode (junction) becomes reverse-biased.

cutoff

The transistor is _____ when emitter current can no longer decrease. At this point, the emitter-

⌄   base diode is reverse-biased.

cut off

⌄   At cutoff, the emitter-base diode is _____.

reverse-biased

When I_e reaches point Z, what type of bias do you

⌄   have at the emitter-base diode? _____.

reverse

When cutoff is reached, the _____ diode is reverse-biased, and collector current ceases to flow

⌄   causing feedback current to cease flowing.

emitter-base

The reverse bias on the ____ - ____ diode causes the emitter current, and therefore the collector cur-

⌄   rent, to cease.

emitter-base

217

The reverse bias will cause feedback to cease as a result of _____ ceasing.

▽

collector current

When the _____ ceases, feedback will cease and the bias conditions begin to revert to their original state.

▽

collector current

Collector current ceases, causing _____ to cease; therefore, the bias conditions begin to revert to their original state.

▽

feedback

The bias conditions begin to revert to their original state as soon as _____ ceases and the process is repeated. Basically, the transistor is driven to _____, then to cutoff, then back to saturation, then to _____, etc.

▽

feedback
saturation
cutoff

The elapsed time for the change from saturation to cutoff is primarily determined by the tank circuit, which in turn, determines the frequency of oscillation. The _____ determines the time for change from saturation to cutoff.

▽

tank circuit

The frequency of oscillation, which is the time it takes the transistor to go from saturation to cutoff, is determined by the _____.

▽

tank circuit

218

The time it takes for the transistor to go from
_____ to cutoff determines the frequency of

⇨   _____.

saturation
oscillation

What controls the frequency of oscillation?

⇨   _____.

tank circuit

set **4** **OSCILLATORS**

The two basic types of oscillators are the tuned *base* and tuned *collector*. The tuned-b＿＿＿＿＿＿ and tuned-c＿＿＿＿＿＿ oscillators are the two basic

▽ types of oscillators.

base
collector

The most common oscillators are the tuned-
▽ ＿＿＿＿＿＿ and tuned-＿＿＿＿＿＿.

base
collector

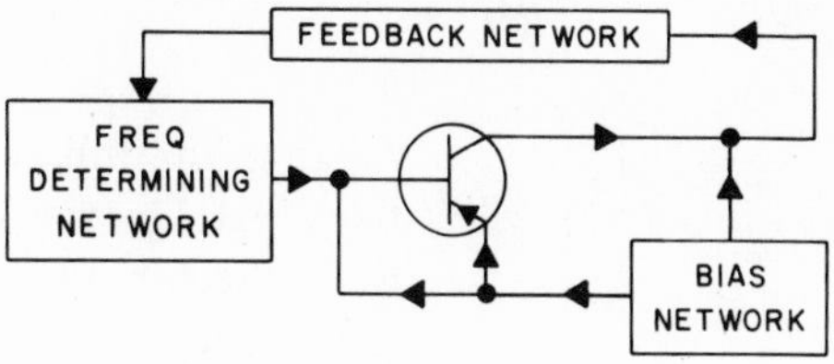

FEEDBACK NETWORK

FREQ
DETERMINING
NETWORK

BIAS
NETWORK

TUNED-BASE OSCILLATOR

Figure 5

The tuned-base oscillator block diagram is shown in Figure 5. The *frequency determining elements* are found in the base circuit. The tuned-＿＿＿＿＿＿ oscillator has the frequency determining elements in

▽ the base circuit.

base

The ＿＿＿＿＿＿ elements are found in the base
▽ circuit for the tuned-base oscillator.

frequency determining

221

▽ Where are the frequency determining elements found for the tuned base? _____.

in the base circuit

Feedback is accomplished from the collector through the feedback network, through the frequency determining elements, to the base. The path from the collector through the feedback network, through the frequency determining elements to the base is called

▽ the _____ path.

feedback

The feedback path is from the c_____ through the f_____ network, through the f_____

▽ d_____ elements to the b_____.

collector
feedback
frequency determining
base

Arrange the following in a logical order for the feedback path in the tuned-base oscillator starting from the collector and working to the base.
(a) through feedback network _____
(b) from collector _____
(c) to the base _____
(d) through frequency determining

▽   elements _____

(b)
(a)
(d)
(c)

The *biasing network* provides emitter-to-base forward bias and collector-to-base reverse bias. The emitter-to-base diode is forward biased and the collector-to-base diode is reverse biased by the _____

▽ _____.

biasing network

222

The _____ determines the bias between the
emitter-base diode and the collector-base diode.

biasing network

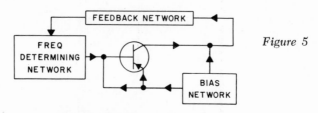

Figure 5

TUNED-BASE OSCILLATOR

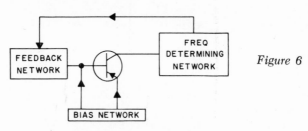

Figure 6

TUNED-COLLECTOR OSCILLATOR

The main difference between the tuned-base and
tuned-collector oscillator is the placement of the *frequency determining* network. The placement of the
_____ network determines the type of oscillator.

frequency determining

The _____ network in a tuned-base oscil-
lator is in the base circuit, while in a tuned-collector
oscillator it is in the collector circuit.

frequency determining

In a *tuned-base* oscillator, the frequency determining
network is in the _____
while a tuned-collector oscillator has the frequency
determining network in the _____
_____.

base circuit
collector circuit

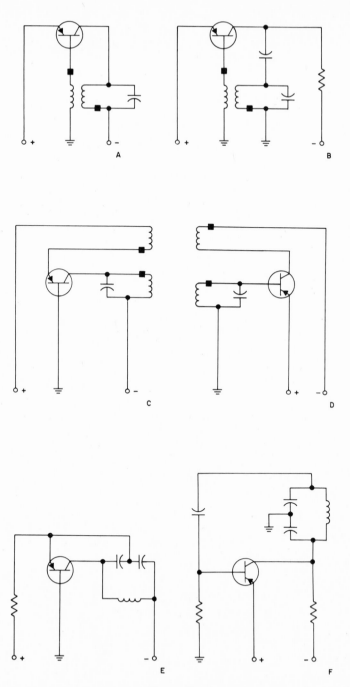

Figure 7

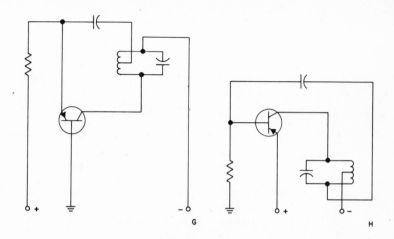

BASIC TRANSISTOR OSCILLATOR CIRCUITS

Figure 7 (continued)

Which circuits in Figure 7 are tuned-collector oscillators? Which are tuned-base oscillators?

Tuned collector
    A
    B
    C
    E
    F
    G
    H

Tuned base
    D

Three of the most common tuned-collector oscillators are the *Colpitts, Clapp,* and *Hartley* oscillators. The _____, _____, and _____ oscillators are three of the most common tuned-collector oscillators.

Colpitts
Clapp
Hartley

225

The Colpitts, Clapp, and Hartley are tuned-
_____ oscillators having their frequency de-
⌁ termining elements in the _____ circuit.

collector
collector

Among tuned-collector oscillators, three of the most
common are: the _____, _____, and
⌁ _____ oscillators.

Colpitts
Clapp
Hartley

The frequency determining network for (the)
_____ (Clapp, Colpitts, Hartley, all three)
⌁ is located in the collector circuit.

all three

The *Colpitts* oscillator uses two series capacitors in
parallel with a coil for a frequency determining network. The feedback is taken from the junction between the two capacitors. Either or both capacitors
may be adjusted to control the frequency and the
amount of feedback.

⌁ *Proceed to the next frame.*

A characteristic of a _____ oscillator is the
⌁ use of a split-capacitance to obtain feedback.

Colpitts

_____ in a Colpitts oscillator is obtained by
⌁ use of split-capacitors.

Feedback

226

A characteristic of a Colpitts oscillator is the use of
_____-_____ to obtain and adjust the amount of
⟁ feedback and the frequency output.

split-capacitors

The amount of feedback and the frequency output
of the Colpitts oscillator can be adjusted by either or
both of the _____ in the frequency deter-
⟁ mining network.

*capacitors (split-capaci-
tors)*

A Colpitts oscillator uses split-_____ (resistors, capacitors, hairs) in the frequency determining
⟁ network.

capacitors

A *Clapp* oscillator is a modified Colpitts, the difference being the addition of a capacitor in series with
the coil in the frequency determining network. By
adding a capacitor in series with the coil in the frequency determining network of a Colpitts oscillator
⟁ you form a _____ oscillator.

Clapp

The main difference between a Clapp oscillator and
a Colpitts is the addition of a _____ in series
⟁ with the coil in the frequency determining network.

capacitor

An oscillator with split-capacitors in parallel with a
coil and a capacitor for a frequency determining net-
⟁ work is a _____ oscillator.

Clapp

227

A frequency determining network which consists of split-capacitors in parallel with a _____ and a coil is a characteristic of a Clapp oscillator.

capacitor

The use of a capacitor in series with the coil in the frequency determining network is the main difference between a _____ and a _____ oscillator.

Clapp
Colpitts
(either order)

A Clapp oscillator has _____ - _____ in _____ (parallel, series) with a capacitor and coil for a frequency determining network.

split-capacitors
parallel

Can you tell the difference between a Clapp oscillator and a Colpitts oscillator? _____.

If you can't, you had better review the preceding frames.

A *Hartley* oscillator is similar to the Colpitts with the exception that split-inductance is used instead of split-capacitance to obtain feedback. The _____ oscillator uses split-inductance to obtain feedback.

Hartley

A characteristic of the _____ oscillator is the use of split-inductance to obtain the feedback.

Hartley

228

An outstanding difference between the Hartley and Colpitts oscillators is the method of obtaining

⟁ _____.

feedback

Feedback is obtained in the Hartley oscillator by the

⟁ use of _____-_____ .

split-inductance

Split-_____ (inductance, capacitance) is used in the _____ (Colpitts, Clapp, Hartley) type

⟁ oscillator to obtain feedback.

inductance
Hartley
or
Capacitance
Colpitts

Draw the frequency determining networks for the following type oscillators:
(a) Colpitts   (b) Clapp   (c) Hartley

⟁

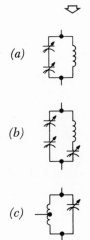

(a)

(b)

(c)

229

PART FIVE
MODULATION-DEMODULATION

set **1** **MODULATION**

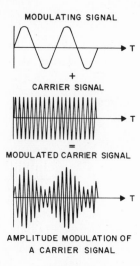

MODULATING SIGNAL

+

CARRIER SIGNAL

=

MODULATED CARRIER SIGNAL

AMPLITUDE MODULATION OF
A CARRIER SIGNAL

Figure 1

Amplitude modulation takes place when the amplitude of a carrier signal is caused to vary in accordance with a modulating signal. (See Figure 1.)

▽   *Proceed to the next frame.*

When the amplitude of a carrier signal is caused to vary in accordance with a modulating signal, the carrier is said to be a _____ m _____ .

amplitude modulated

Varying the _____ of a carrier signal in accordance with a modulating signal is called amplitude modulation.

amplitude

233

A _____ signal is amplitude modulated when its amplitude is made to vary in accordance with a _____ signal.

⇩

carrier
modulating

What is the process of varying the amplitude of a carrier signal at a modulating signal rate called?

⇩ _____.

amplitude modulation

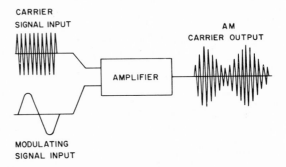

CARRIER
SIGNAL INPUT

AM
CARRIER OUTPUT

AMPLIFIER

MODULATING
SIGNAL INPUT

Figure 2a

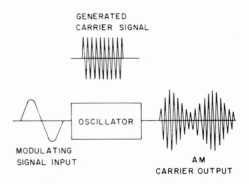

GENERATED
CARRIER SIGNAL

OSCILLATOR

MODULATING
SIGNAL INPUT

AM
CARRIER OUTPUT

METHODS OF OBTINING AMPLITUDE MODULATION

Figure 2b

234

Amplitude modulation can be accomplished by using an *amplifier* or an *oscillator*. Name two devices that may be used for amplitude modulation. (See Figure 2.) _____   _____.

⇩

oscillator
amplifier
(either order)

Oscillator circuits or _____ circuits can be used to accomplish amplitude modulation.

⇩

amplifier

Either a(n) _____ or a(n) _____ can be used to amplitude modulate a _____ wave.

⇩

oscillator⎫
amplifier⎬ *(either order)*

carrier

An amplifier circuit can be used to amplitude modulate a carrier by applying a constant level carrier signal to the amplifier and varying the *bias* at the modulating signal rate. When an amplifier is used as a modulator, the b_____ is varied at the modulating signal rate.

⇩

bias

In the amplifier method of producing amplitude modulation, a constant level carrier signal is applied to the amplifier while the _____ is varied at the modulating signal rate.

⇩

bias

In an amplifier amplitude modulator, the bias is varied at the _____ (modulating, carrier) signal rate.

⇩

modulating

235

The _____ is varied at a _____
signal rate while the _____ is held at a constant level in an amplifier amplitude modulator.

bias
modulating
carrier

The varying bias is said to _____ the carrier
signal in an amplifier amplitude modulator.

modulate

How does amplitude modulation of a carrier signal
take place in an amplifier? _____.

A constant level carrier
signal is fed into an amp-
lifier whose bias is varied
in accordance with a
modulating signal. This
results in an amplitude
modulated (AM) carrier
signal — or merely an
AM signal for brevity.

The varying bias causes the *gain* of an amplifier to
vary at a modulating signal rate while a carrier is fed
through the amplifier, thus amplitude modulating the
carrier.

Proceed to the next frame.

By varying the bias of an amplifier at a modulating
signal rate, you can vary the _____ of the
amplifier at the modulating signal rate.

gain

The _____ of an amplifier can be made to vary at a _____ signal rate by varying the bias at a modulating signal rate.

⬦

gain
modulating

If the _____ of an amplifier is varying at a _____ signal rate because the _____ is varying at such a rate, the amplitude of the output must be varying at the same rate.

⬦

gain
modulating
bias

By varying the _____, and hence, the gain of an _____ at a _____ signal rate while a carrier is being passed through the amplifier, you can amplitude _____ the _____.

⬦

bias
amplifier
modulating
modulate
carrier

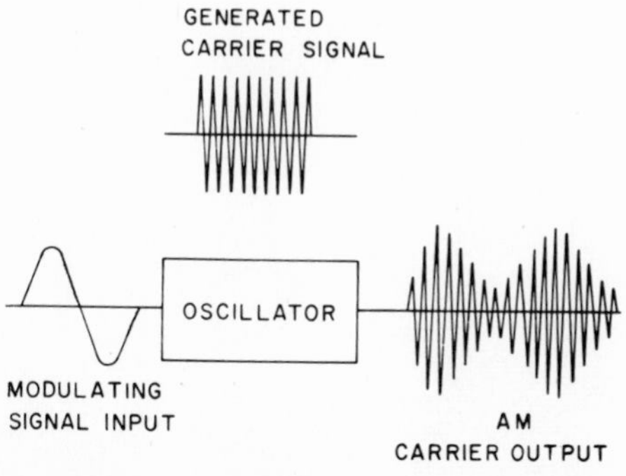

GENERATED
CARRIER SIGNAL

OSCILLATOR

MODULATING
SIGNAL INPUT

AM
CARRIER OUTPUT

METHODS OF OBTINING AMPLITUDE MODULATION

Figure 2b

An *oscillator* can also be used as an amplitude modulator by varying the bias of the oscillator at a _____ signal rate. (See Figure 2b.)

⬦

modulating

237

The bias of an oscillator can be varied at a
_____ signal rate, therefore causing the car-
▽ rier to be _____.

An oscillator can be amplitude modulated by
▽ _____ the bias at a modulating signal rate.

To produce amplitude modulation using an oscillator
as a modulator, you _____ (cut off, clamp,
▽ vary) the bias at a modulating signal rate.

Which of the following would you use to produce
amplitude modulation (pick two)? _____.
(1) resistor   (3) oscillator
(2) logic circuits   (4) cement mixer
▽   (5) amplifier

set # ⨶ MODULATING WITH TRANSISTORS

A carrier signal may be amplitude modulated (AM) by injecting a modulating signal into the base, the emitter, or the _____.

collector

The modulating signal can be injected into the base, the emitter, or the collector to _____ modulate a carrier signal.

amplitude

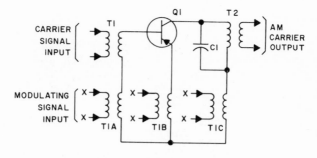

CARRIER SIGNAL INPUT

MODULATING SIGNAL INPUT

METHODS OF INJECTING AMPLITUDE MODULATING SIGNAL INTO AMPLIFIER CIRCUIT

Figure 3

In Figure 3, transformer T1A, T1B, or T1C provide b _____, e _____, or c _____ injection, respectively.

base
emitter
collector

239

Each method of injecting the modulating signal will vary the bias and therefore the gain of the amplifier.

▽ *Proceed to the next frame.*

A change in the bias changes the ＿＿＿＿＿＿ of the amplifier.

gain

Any change in ＿＿＿＿＿＿ changes the ＿＿＿＿＿＿ of an amplifier which results in a varying ＿＿＿＿＿＿ (amplitude, shape, static) in the output signal.

▽

bias
gain
amplitude

Changes in the ＿＿＿＿＿＿ of the output signal of an amplifier are a direct result of the variations in the gain which are caused by changes in the

▽ ＿＿＿＿＿＿.

amplitude
bias

Modulating the bias of an amplifier will vary the gain, thereby ＿＿＿＿＿＿ the output of the am-plifier.

▽

amplitude modulating

When emitter injection or base injection is used, the level of the input carrier must always be less than the emitter-base bias. If this were not the case, the bias would be determined by the carrier, not the modulating signal, and the result would be distortion.

▽ *Proceed to the next frame.*

240

the input carrier level must always be
_____ (less, greater) than the emitter-base
bias when an amplifier is modulated with emitter
▽ injection or base injection.

less

When emitter or base injection is used to modulate
an amplifier the input carrier level must be
▽ _____ than the emitter-base bias.

less

Unless the _____ level were less than the
emitter-base bias, the modulated output would be
▽ *distorted.*

carrier

The modulated output would be _____ if
the carrier level were not less than the
_____-_____ bias when _____ injection
▽ or _____ injection modulation is used.

distorted
emitter-base
emitter⎫
base ⎬ *(either order)*

Low-level modulation can be used with base, emitter,
or collector injection, but high-level modulation
should only be used with collector injection. If high-
level modulation were used with emitter or base injection, the modulated output would be distorted.
What level of modulation should be used with base
▽ injection or emitter injection? _____.

low-level

If _____ (low-level, high-level) modulation were used with b_____ or e_____ injection, the modulated output would be distorted.

↬ *high-level*
    base
    emitter

Low-level modulation can be used with _____, _____, or _____ injection.

↬ *base*
    collector
    emitter
    (any order)

Collector injection will give satisfactory modulation with low-level or high-level modulation. High-level or low-level modulation can be used with _____ to give satisfactory modulation.

↬ *collector injection*

Satisfactory modulation can be obtained with low-level or high-level modulation when _____ is used.

↬ *collector injection*

High-level modulation should *not* be used with _____ (emitter and base, collector and base) injection.

↬ *emitter and base*

High-level modulation can be used with _____ without causing distortion.

↬ *collector injection*

242

If high-level modulation were used with base injection, the output modulation would be _____ (distortion free, distorted).

↔

distorted

What type injection would you use to high-level modulate an amplifier? _____.

↔

collector injection

What type of injection would you use to low-level modulate an amplifier? _____.

↔

any kind

set **3**

FREQUENCY MODULATION

Frequency Modulation (FM) is accomplished by varying the _____ of an oscillator at the modulating rate.

▽

frequency

A carrier is _____ by varying the frequency of an oscillator at the modulating rate.

▽

frequency modulated

Frequency modulation can be accomplished by varying the resonant _____ of the oscillator tank circuit at a _____ rate.

▽

frequency
modulating

By varying the frequency determining circuit of an oscillator at a modulating rate, you can _____ the output signal.

▽

frequency modulate

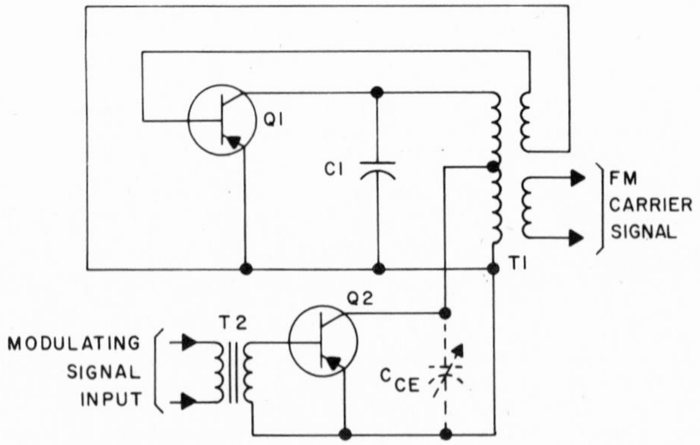

OSCILLATOR CIRCUIT, FREQUENCY MODULATED

Figure 4

244

Figure 4 shows an oscillator circuit that is frequency modulated by *reactance modulation*. The modulating signal, coupled through transformer _____, varies the emitter-base bias of Q2. Q2 is a reactance modulator.

▽

T2

The _____-_____ bias of the reactance modulator is varied by the modulating signal.

▽

emitter-base

The modulating signal varies the _____-_____ of reactance modulator Q2, causing the collector voltage of Q2 to vary at the same rate.

▽

emitter-base bias

As the emitter-base bias of Q2 increases and decreases at the modulating rate, the _____ voltage will vary at the same rate.

▽

output (collector)

The collector voltage of Q2 _____ (will, will not) vary directly with the emitter-base bias for the common-emitter configuration.

▽

will

The collector voltage _____ (increases, decreases) as the emitter-base bias decreases.

▽

decreases

As the collector voltage of Q2 increases, output capacitance C_{CE}* decreases, and as the collector voltage decreases, the C_{CE} increases; therefore C_{CE} will vary at the modulating rate. Output capacitance C_{CE} varies _____ (inversely, directly) with the collector voltage of Q2.

▽   *Capacitance between collector and emitter (inside transistor).

inversely

245

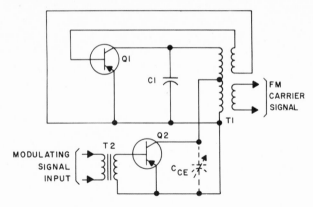

OSCILLATOR CIRCUIT, FREQUENCY MODULATED

Figure 4

A decrease in input to Q2 results in a decrease in the collector voltage, but the _____ _____ will increase.

⮑

output capacitance

The _____ (use symbol) of Q2 will decrease due to an increase in collector voltage.

⮑

C_{CE} *(output capacitance)*

The C_{CE} of Q2 affects the *resonant frequency* of the tank circuit of oscillator Q1. C_{CE} is changing at the modulating rate; therefore the output frequency of Q1 will be changing at the modulating rate.

⮑ *Proceed to the next frame.*

The r_____ f_____ of the tank circuit of oscillator Q1 will be changing at the same rate of C_{CE}.

⮑

resonant frequency

⮑ At what rate is C_{CE} varying? _____.

We're learning modulation; therefore, C_{CE} is varying at the modulating rate.

246

If the _____ frequency of the tank circuit of Q1 is varying at the modulating rate, the frequency of the output signal of Q1 will vary at the same rate.

resonant

The resonant frequency of the _____ _____ of Q1 will vary at the _____ rate.

tank circuit
modulating

The resonant frequency of the tank circuit of Q1 determines the output frequency of oscillator Q1. The _____ frequency of oscillator Q1 will be dependent upon the _____ frequency of the tank circuit of Q1.

output
resonant

The frequency at which the tank circuit of Q1 is _____ will be the _____ frequency of oscillator Q1.

resonant (oscillating)
output

The resonant frequency of the tank circuit of Q1 is varying at the same rate as C_{CE} which is varying at the _____ rate; therefore, the output frequency is varying at the _____ rate.

modulating
modulating

When the output frequency of Q1 is varying at the _____ rate, the output of Q1 is _____ modulated.

modulating
frequency

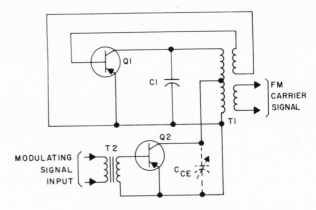

OSCILLATOR CIRCUIT, FREQUENCY MODULATED

Figure 4

Q1 is frequency _____ when its output _____ is varying at a modulating rate.

modulated
frequency

DEMODULATION

One type of demodulation, or detection is Continuous Wave (CW) detection. CW detection is accomplished by *heterodyning* the carrier signal with the output of an oscillator to produce an audio signal. The process of detection which beats the output of an oscillator with the CW carrier signal is called h_____.

heterodyning

A _____ signal is detected by heterodyning the carrier signal with the output of an oscillator.

CW

The oscillator used to h_____ the CW signal in a superheterodyne receiver is called a beat frequency oscillator.

heterodyne

A _____ oscillator is used in a superheterodyne receiver for CW detection.

beat frequency

A CW signal is detected by _____ the carrier signal with the output of a _____.

heterodyning
beat frequency oscillator

A second type of detection is Amplitude Modulation (AM) detection. The AM detector *rectifies* and *filters* the _____ variations of the signal.

amplitude

249

The prime functions of an AM detector are to
r_____y and f_____r the amplitude
⬦   variations of an AM signal.

rectify
filter

An _____ rectifies and filters the _____
⬦   variations of an AM signal.

AM detector
amplitude

AM detection may be accomplished by using a diode
or a transistor.

⬦   *Proceed to the next frame.*

A third type of detection is Frequency Modulation
(FM) detection. The FM carrier signal is applied
to the FM detector which rectifies and filters the
⬦   _____ variations of the carrier signal.

frequency

The prime functions of an FM detector are to
_____ and _____ the _____
⬦   variations of an FM signal.

rectify
filter
frequency

FM detection may be accomplished by employing a
discriminator or a slope detector.

⬦   *Proceed to the next frame.*

250

Name the three types of detection and match them
with their function from the list on the right.

(1) _____ Rectifies and filters the amplitude variations of the applied
carrier signal.

(2) _____ Heterodynes the carrier signal
with the output of an oscillator.

(3) _____ Rectifies and filters the frequency variation of the applied
carrier signal.

⬦

(1) AM detection
(2) CW detection
(3) FM detection

If you have erred on the previous frame, it would be
advantageous to review this set again. If not, proceed
⬦ to the next set.

set **5**   **AM DEMODULATION;**
DIODE DETECTOR

⇩ What does an AM detector do (how is detection accomplished)? _____.

An AM dectector rectifies
and filters the amplitude.

⇩ Diode detectors provide a *voltage* output or a *current* output. The two outputs that a diode detector may provide are _____ and _____.

voltage
current
(either order)

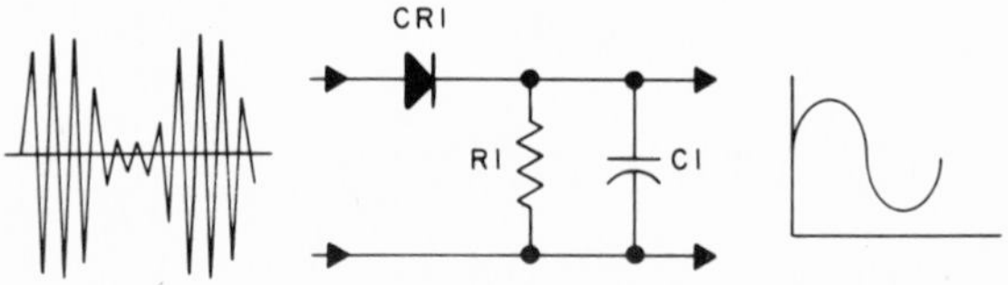

VOLTAGE DETECTION

Figure 5

⇩ The circuit shown in Figure 5 is a voltage output-type diode detector. Diode CR1 is the rectifying device, resistor *R1* is the load, and capacitor C1 is the filter. The filter, load, and rectifier are _____, _____, and _____, respectively.

C1
R1
CR1

⇩ Diode CR1 _____ the carrier signal since it conducts only on one half of a cycle.

rectifies

252

When _____ conducts, current flows through
▽ resistor R1.

CR1

Current flow through resistor R1 is caused by the
▽ _____ of diode CR1.

conduction

Capacitor C1 charges to the voltage drop across resistor R1 and discharges through R1 when diode CR1
▽ is not _____.

conducting

Conduction of diode CR1 causes C1 to _____
▽ to the voltage drop across _____.

charge
R1

When CR1 does not conduct, C1 _____
▽ through R1.

discharges

The time constant of R1 and C1 prevents C1 from
discharging completely before the next alternation
of the carrier signal. C1 _____ (will, will not)
▽ discharge completely between cycles.

will not

When diode CR1 again conducts, C1 _____
▽ to the voltage drop across R1.

charges

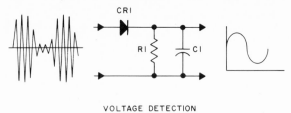

VOLTAGE DETECTION

Figure 5

The _____ and _____ of C1 filters
the output voltage which is essentially increasing and
decreasing with the amplitude changes of the carrier
▽ signal.

charge
discharge

_____ acts to filter the output voltage of the
▽ detector.

C1

The output voltage of the detector is _____
▽ by capacitor C1.

filtered

We can say that amplitude changes of the carrier
signal produce _____ changes in the output
▽ of the voltage detector.

voltage (amplitude)

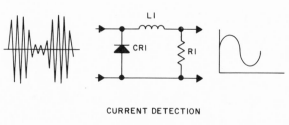

CURRENT DETECTION

Figure 6

A current output-type diode detector is shown in Figure 6. This type of detector may be used with transistors since transistors are current amplifying devices.

▽ *Proceed to the next frame.*

In the circuit shown in Figure 6, diode CR1 is the rectifying device, resistor R1 is the load, and choke L1 is the filter. In Figure 6, the rectifier, filter, and load are _____, _____, and ▽ _____, respectively.

CR1
L1
R1

When diode CR1 conducts it appears as a short circuit _____ (zero, maximum) current flows ▽ through R1.

zero

When CR1 conducts, current _____ (does, ▽ does not) flow through R1.

does not

The current changes in the output of the current detector are dependent on the _____ changes ▽ of the carrier signal.

amplitude

In the voltage detector the filtering element is ▽ _____.

C1

In the current detector the filtering element is ▽ _____.

L1

255

AM DEMODULATION;
TRANSISTOR DETECTOR

In a transistor detector, rectification takes place in the *emitter-base* portion of the transistor. The _____-_____ portion of the transistor, in a transistor detector, acts as a rectifier.

▽

emitter-base

Rectification takes place in the _____-_____ portion of the transistor.

▽

emitter-base

The emitter-base portion of the transistor provides _____ of the carrier signal.

▽

rectification

Amplification takes place in the *emitter-collector* or the *base-collector* portion of the transistor depending on the circuit used. Amplification in a transistor detector takes place at either the _____-_____ or _____-_____ portion of the transistor.

▽

emitter-collector
base-collector
(either order)

Either the emitter-collector portion or the _____-_____ portion of the transistor will provide _____ in a transistor detector.

▽

base-collector
amplification

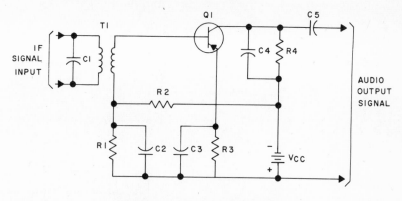

COMMON–EMITTER TRANSISTOR DETECTOR

Figure 7

Figure 7 shows the circuit of a common-emitter transistor detector.

▽   *Proceed to the next frame.*

The i-f signal applied to the base-emitter circuit (biased for nonlinear operation) is rectified by the diode portion, base-emitter, of detector Q1. The applied i-f signal is rectified by the _____ -

▽   portion of Q1.

base-emitter

The diode portion of detector Q1 is the _____ - _____ circuit.

▽

base-emitter

The diode portion of detector Q1 _____ s the

▽   applied i-f signal.

rectifies

Resistor R1 acts as the diode *load* resistor and capacitor C2 *filters* the i-f voltage change. The purpose of R1 and C2 is to act as a _____ resistor and

▽   to _____ the voltage changes, respectively.

load
filter

257

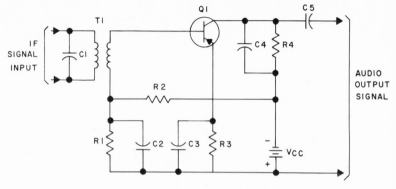

COMMON–EMITTER TRANSISTOR DETECTOR

Figure 7

▽ The i-f filter is composed of components
_____ and _____.

R1
C2

▽ The input circuit acts as a voltage output-type
_____ detector.

diode

▽ The *base-emitter* bias (audio voltage) developed
across R1 causes the collector current to vary at the
audio rate. The collector current varies because of the
_____ - _____ bias voltage developed across R1.

base-emitter

▽ The audio voltage developed across R1 causes the
_____ current to vary at the audio rate.

collector

▽ The combination of the diode portion of Q1, R1, and
C2 change the i-f signal to an _____ voltage.

audio

258

The amplified *audio* signal developed across resistor R4 is coupled through capacitor C5 to the following stage. The amplified _____ signal is developed across R4.

⟁

audio

The emitter-collector circuit of Q1 _____ the audio signal that has been detected in the base-emitter circuit.

⟁

amplifies

Capacitor C1 and the primary of transformer T1 form a *parallel* resonant circuit for the i-f signal. C1 and the primary of T1 form a _____ resonant circuit for the applied i-f signal.

⟁

parallel

The i-f signal is applied to a _____ _____ circuit composed of C1 and the _____ of T1.

⟁

parallel resonant primary

The i-f signal is coupled through T1 to the base-emitter circuit of Q1. T1 serves as a _____ transformer.

⟁

coupling

Resistor R1 is the emitter-base *biasing* resistor and resistor R2 is a voltage dropping resistor. The purpose of R1 is to provide emitter-base _____.

⟁

biasing

⟁ R2 acts as a _____ dropping resistor.

voltage

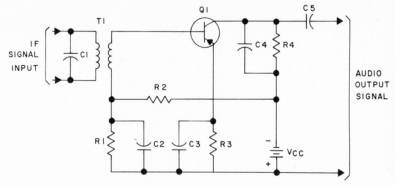

COMMON−EMITTER TRANSISTOR DETECTOR

Figure 7

Capacitors C2 and C4 are bypass capacitors for the *intermediate frequency.* C2 and C4 act as

▽ _____-_____ bypass capacitors.

i-f

Capacitors C3 is an AC bypass capacitor, resistor R3 is the emitter swamping resistor, and resistor R4 is the collector load resistor.

▽ *Proceed to the next frame.*

▽ The collector load resistor is _____.

R4

▽ The emitter swamping resistor is _____.

R3

▽ The AC bypass capacitor is _____.

C3

Capacitor *C5* couples the audio output signal and blocks the DC voltage from the following stage. The audio output signal is coupled to the following stage by _____.

⇨

C5

C5 also blocks the _____ voltage from the following stage.

⇨

DC

Capacitor **C5** serves two purposes:
(1) _____.   (2) _____.

⇨

(1) couples audio output signal to following stages (2) blocks DC voltage from following stage

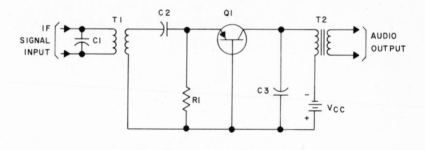

COMMON–BASE TRANSISTOR DETECTOR

Figure 8

Figure 8 shows a common-base transistor detector. Detection takes place in the *emitter-base* circuit of transistor detector Q1. The _____-_____ circuit of Q1 detects the i-f input signal.

⇨

emitter-base

261

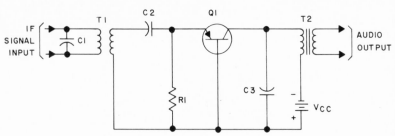

COMMON–BASE TRANSISTOR DETECTOR

Figure 8

    The i-f signal is _____ in the emitter-base circuit of Q1.

detected (rectified)

    Amplification takes place in the collector-base circuit of transistor detector Q1. The ___-___ circuit of Q1 amplifies the detected audio signal.

collector-base

    The detected audio signal is _____ in the collector-base circuit of Q1.

amplified

    When the polarity of the i-f signal is positive on the emitter, current flows through the emitter-base circuit. Current _____ (will, will not) flow through the emitter-base circuit when the emitter of Q1 is positive.

will

    A _____ polarity i-f signal on the emitter of Q1 will cause current to flow in the _____-base circuit.

positive
emitter-base

Capacitor C2 *charges* on the positive alternation, and *discharges* through R1 on the negative alternation. On the positive alternation, C2 _____ and on the negative alternation _____ through R1.

charges
discharges

The polarity of the i-f signal determines whether C2 will _____ or _____.

charge
discharge

The long *time constant* of C2 and R1 does not allow C2 to discharge much during the negative alternation. The amount of discharge of C2 is determined by the _____ of C2 and R1.

time constant

Because of the long _____ of C2 and R1, C2 will not discharge very much during the negative alternation.

time constant

C2 _____ (will, will not) discharge very much during the negative alternation.

will not

The next positive alternation again charges C2 with the result that the peaks of the positive alternations are *filtered* by C2. The positive peaks of the i-f signal are _____ by C2.

filtered

The long time constant of R1 and C2 enable C2 to _____ the positive peaks of the i-f signal.

filter

263

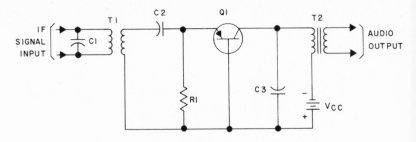

COMMON–BASE TRANSISTOR DETECTOR

Figure 8

The bias between the emitter and base becomes a DC voltage with an *audio* voltage component. The emitter-base bias voltage is a voltage varying at the _____ rate.

↶ *audio*

The filtering of the i-f signal results in an _____ voltage being impressed on a DC voltage level in the _____ -base circuit of Q1.

↶ *audio*
emitter-base

From the preceding, we see that the *amplitude* changes of the i-f signal are detected in the emitter-base circuit of Q1. The emitter-base circuit detects the _____ changes of the i-f signal.

↶ *amplitude*

Since the bias of the emitter-base circuit is changing at the audio rate, the *collector* current also varies at the audio rate. A change in amplitude of the emitter-base bias gives a corresponding change in amplitude of the _____ current.

↶ *collector*

264

The _____ current varies at the same rate
▽ as the emitter-base bias.

collector

If the emitter-base bias varies at an audio rate, the
▽ _____ also varies at the same audio rate.

collector current

Capacitor C3 filters out any variations of the *i-f* signal
present in the collector current. C3 serves as an
_____ bypass capacitor in the collector cir-
▽ cuit.

i-f

set 7

FM DEMODULATION; DISCRIMINATOR

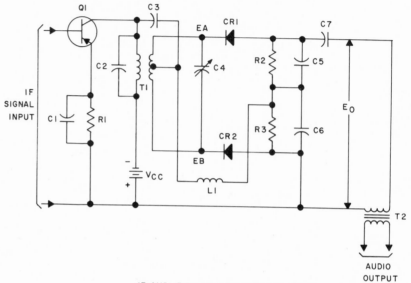

IF AMPLIFIER AND DISCRIMINATOR STAGE

Figure 9

Figure 9 shows a transistorized version of an i-f stage and a discriminator.

▽ *Proceed to the next frame.*

A discriminator in an FM receiver performs the same function as a *detector* in an AM receiver. An FM discriminator performs the same function as an AM

▽ _____.

detector

The function of an FM _____ is _____ (the same as, different from) the function of an AM

▽ _____.

discriminator
the same as
detector

Amplifier Q1 (Figure 9) *amplifies* the i-f signal applied to the discriminator. Q1 _____ the applied i-f signal.

⇨

amplifies

The i-f signal _____ by Q1 is _____ by the discriminator circuit (Figure 9).

⇨

amplified
detected

Capacitor C2 and the primary of transformer T1 form a *parallel* resonant circuit which is resonant at the unmodulated carrier frequency f_0. C2 and the primary of T1 form a _____ resonant circuit.

⇨

parallel

The _____ resonant circuit formed by C2 and the primary of T1 is resonant at the unmodulated carrier frequency f_0.

⇨

parallel

The parallel resonant circuit, C2 and primary of T1, resonates at _____.

⇨

f_0

The _____ resonant circuit formed by capacitor _____ and the _____ of T1 is resonant at the _____ (modulated, unmodulated) carrier frequency _____.

⇨

parallel
C2
primary
unmodulated
f_0

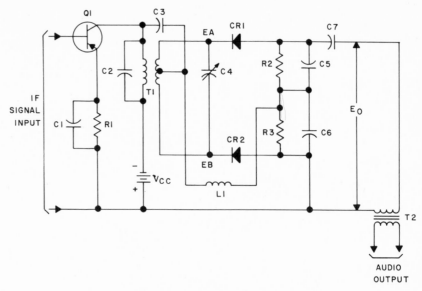

IF AMPLIFIER AND DISCRIMINATOR STAGE

Figure 9

The circuit formed by C4 and the secondary of T1 also forms a _____ resonant circuit which is resonant to f_0.

↜ *parallel*

The parallel resonant circuit formed by C4 and the secondary of T1 is also resonant to _____.

↜ f_0

Capacitor C3 couples the i-f signal to the secondary of T1 for *phase shift* comparison. The i-f signal is coupled to the secondary of T1 to provide _____ comparison.

↜ *phase shift*

By comparing the i-f signal at the primary of T1 to that at the secondary of T1, it is possible to determine the _____ of the signal.

↜ *phase shift*

The amount of phase shift across T1 for an unmodulated carrier frequency (f_0) is 90° due to the use of an air core transformer. If the applied i-f signal is at f_0, the phase shift across T1 is _____.

If the i-f frequency becomes greater than f_0, the phase shift across T1 will be greater than _____ degrees.

If the i-f frequency becomes less than f_0, the phase shift across T1 will be _____ (greater, less) than 90°.

The amount of phase shift across T1 _____ (is, is not) dependent on the amount that the i-f frequency varies from f_0.

The top half of T1 secondary, diode CR1, coil L1, load resistor R2, and filter capacitor C5 form one half of the *comparison* network. One half of the _____ network is composed of the top half of T1 secondary, CR1, L1, R2, and C5.

The bottom half of T1 secondary, diode CR2, coil L1, load resistor R3, and filter capacitor C6 form the other half of the _____ network.

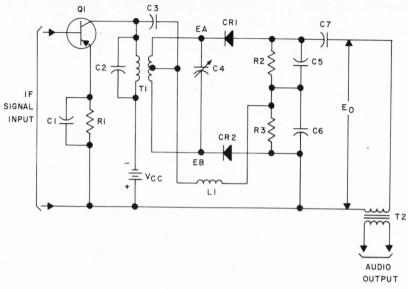

IF AMPLIFIER AND DISCRIMINATOR STAGE

Figure 9

The 90° phase shift at the resonant frequency f_0 results in two voltages, E_A and E_B, having *equal* amplitudes. At 90° phase shift, the amplitude of E_A

⬦ _____ the amplitude of E_B.

equals

At 90° phase shift the _____ s of E_A and E_B

⬦ are equal.

amplitudes (voltages)

When the incoming signal is frequency modulated, the i-f frequency is either greater than f_0 or less than

⬦ _____.

f_0

If the i-f frequency is either *greater* or *less* than f_0, the phase shift across T1 is either _____ or _____ than 90° because of the reactive

⬦ characteristics of the circuits for signals off resonance.

greater
less

270

↻ The phase shift across T1 is controlled by the modulated _____ frequency.

i-f (carrier)

↻ When the phase shift across T1 is greater than 90°,
E_B exceeds E_A in magnitude. E_B exceeds E_A in magnitude when the phase shift is _____ than 90°.

greater

↻ The p_____ s_____ of the i-f signal
is determined by comparing the signals applied to
both the _____ and _____ wind-
ings of T1.

phase shift
primary
secondary

↻ If the phase shift across T1 becomes greater than
90°, the magnitude of E_B will become _____
than the magnitude of E_A.

greater

$$E_A = 3 \text{ volts} \qquad E_B = 5 \text{ volts}$$
↻ The phase shift across T1 is _____ (greater,
less) than 90°.

greater

↻ When the phase shift is less than 90°, the magnitude
of E_A exceeds E_B. The magnitude of E_A exceeds the
magnitude of E_B when the phase shift is _____
than 90°.

less

$$E_A = 6 \text{ volts} \qquad E_B = 4 \text{ volts}$$
↻ The phase shift across T1 is _____ (greater,
less) than 90°.

less

271

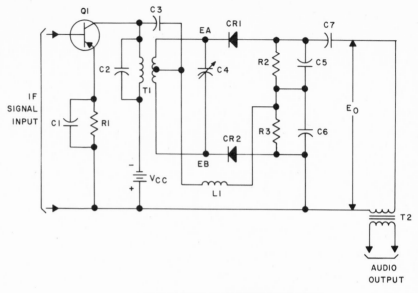

IF AMPLIFIER AND DISCRIMINATOR STAGE

Figure 9

The important item to remember in the discriminator action is that E_A and E_B are unequal for any input signal frequency except the average unmodulated frequency f_0.

▽ *Proceed to the next frame.*

The changes in carrier frequency above and below f_0 have a direct bearing on the relative magnitudes of

▽ _____ and _____.

E_A
E_B

The AM detector portion with the two crystal diodes CR1 and CR2 is arranged so that the available output voltage E_o is equal to the difference between E_A and E_B. Thus we can say that _____ $= E_B - E_A$.

E_o

272

When the input signal is the unmodulated carrier at frequency f_0, the output voltage E_o is:
$$E_o = E_B - E_A = \underline{\hspace{3cm}}.$$

⟁

0 (zero)

When the carrier frequency is greater than f_0, the voltage difference between E_A and E_B is positive $(+E_o)$, and when the carrier frequency is less than f_0, the voltage difference between E_A and E_B is negative $(-E_o)$.

⟁ *Proceed to the next frame.*

If E_o is +5 volts, the carrier frequency is

⟁ $\underline{\hspace{3cm}}$ (greater, less) than f_0.

greater

If E_o is −5 volts, the $\underline{\hspace{3cm}}$ is $\underline{\hspace{3cm}}$

⟁ (greater, less) than f_0.

carrier frequency
less

A change in carrier frequency will give a change in

⟁ $\underline{\hspace{3cm}}$.

E_o

As a result of the actions of the phase discriminator and of the AM detector, the output voltage will vary

⟁ at the m $\underline{\hspace{3cm}}$ rate.

modulating

The audio output is taken from the top of capacitor C5 and the bottom of capacitor C6. The output of

⟁ this circuit is an $\underline{\hspace{3cm}}$ output.

audio

273

set **8**

FM DEMODULATION;
SLOPE DETECTOR

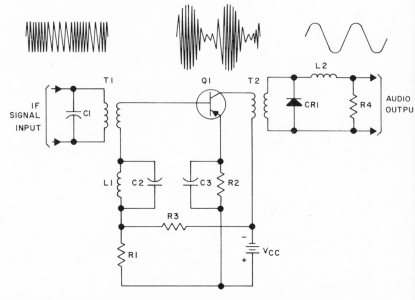

SLOPE DETECTOR AND DIODE DETECTOR

Figure 10

Figure 10 shows a slope detector and diode detector with input and output waveforms of the slope detector and the AM diode detector.

▽ *Proceed to the next frame.*

A *slope detector* converts the frequency changes of a carrier signal into amplitude changes. Frequency changes in a carrier signal are converted into amplitude changes by a _____.

▽

slope detector

A ＿＿＿＿＿＿ converts frequency changes into amplitude changes.

▽

slope detector

＿＿＿＿＿＿ changes in a carrier signal are converted into ＿＿＿＿＿＿ changes by a slope detector.

▽

Frequency
amplitude

A slope detector changes a ＿＿＿＿＿＿ modulated signal into an ＿＿＿＿＿＿ modulated signal.

▽

frequency
amplitude

The resultant amplitude modulated signal from the slope detector is then detected by a(n) ＿＿＿＿＿＿ (AM, FM) detector.

▽

AM

The output of slope detector Q1 (Figure 10) is an i-f signal with both frequency and ＿＿＿＿＿＿ deviations.

▽

amplitude

The resonant circuit consisting of coil L1 and capacitor C2 (tuned slightly off carrier frequency) develops a *large* amount of i-f signal when the frequency deviation of the i-f input is near the resonant frequency. The amount of i-f signal developed is ＿＿＿＿＿＿ when the frequency deviation of the i-f input is near the resonant frequency.

▽

large

275

The amount of i-f signal developed by the resonant circuit depends on the frequency d_____ of the input signal.

↻

deviation

As the frequency deviation of the i-f signal becomes lower than the resonant frequency of the tank, a *smaller* amount of i-f signal is developed. The amount of i-f signal developed is _____ when the frequency deviation is lower than the resonant frequency.

↻

smaller

When the frequency deviation is lower than the resonant frequency, the amount of i-f signal developed becomes _____ (smaller, larger).

↻

smaller

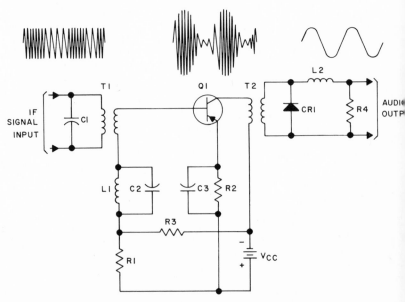

SLOPE DETECTOR AND DIODE DETECTOR

Figure 10

A large amount of i-f signal added to the bias voltage developed across R1 increases the emitter-base bias and a small amount of i-f signal _____ the emitter-base bias.

⇨

decreases

The emitter-base bias _____ when a large amount of *i-f* signal voltage is added to the bias voltage.

⇨

increases

The emitter-base bias _____ when a small amount of _____-_____ signal voltage is added to the bias voltage.

⇨

decreases
i-f

The emitter-base bias is therefore increasing and decreasing as the frequency deviation of the i-f signal _____ and _____, respectively.

⇨

increases
decreases

The emitter-base bias varies directly as the _____ of the i-f signal.

⇨

frequency

As the frequency of the i-f signal increases, the i-f signal developed across R1 _____, and the emitter-base bias _____.

⇨

increases
increases

277

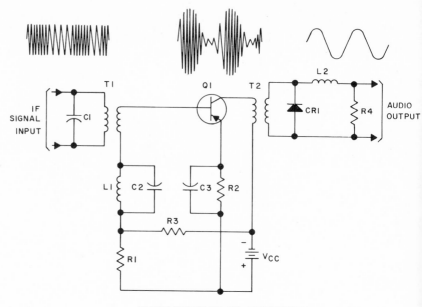

SLOPE DETECTOR AND DIODE DETECTOR

Figure 10

As the frequency of the i-f signal decreases, the i-f signal developed across R1 _____ and the emitter-base bias _____.

decreases
decreases

Therefore, the bias of slope detector Q1 changes at the _____ deviation rate of the i-f signal.

frequency

Since the bias of slope detector Q1 changes at the frequency deviation rate, the gain of Q1 also changes at the _____ rate.

frequency deviation

The gain of slope detector Q1 changed directly as the b_____ of Q1.

bias

278

The output of the slope detector is an i-f signal that
⟳ is changing in both frequency and _____.

amplitude

The i-f signal applied to diode detector CR1 is
rectified, filtered by coil L2, and developed across
R4. The output of the current output-type diode
⟳ detector is an _____ signal.

audio

The resultant output of the circuit in Figure 10 is
an _____ signal that is equivalent to the
⟳ _____ deviations of the i-f input signal.

audio
frequency

PART SIX

TRANSISTOR PULSE AND SWITCHING CIRCUITS

MECHANICAL SWITCHES VERSUS TRANSISTOR SWITCHES

When a switch is open (de-energized), current
_____ (will, will not) flow. When a switch
is closed (energized), current _____ (will,
✧ will not) flow.

will not
will

A device that mechanically controls current flow is
✧ called a _____.

switch

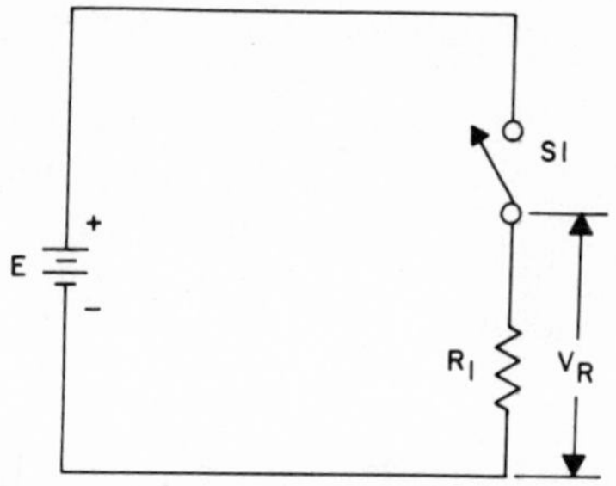

Figure 1

With the switch, S1, in Figure 1, at the position
✧ shown, current _____ (will, will not) flow.

will not

Switch S1, Figure 1, is shown in the _____
✧ position.

open (de-energized)

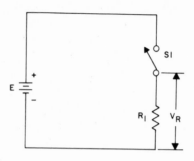

Figure 1

When S1 is open there is no current flow through R1 and the voltage drop (V_r) will therefore be

⋺ _____ volts.

In this case the switch, S1, was _____ to

⋺ cut off the current.

With the switch contacts of S1 in the closed position, current _____ (will, will not) flow. (See

⋺ Figure 1.)

The voltage drop (V_r) will equal _____

⋺ volts.

In this case S1 was _____ to allow the cur-

⋺ rent to flow.

S1 may be _____ to allow current to flow

⋺ or _____ to cut off the current.

The voltage drop (V_r) across resistor R1 has two discrete levels, _____ and _____

⇨ volts.

zero

E

V_r will equal _____ volts when S1 is open

⇨ and _____ volts when S1 is closed.

zero

E

Because of their moving parts, mechanical switches have *slow* switching speed. Mechanical switches are restricted in computer circuits because of their

⇨ _____ switching speed.

slow

A transistor circuit can be designed to take the place of a mechanical switch. Because a transistor has no moving parts, it has _____ (fast, slow)

⇨ switching speeds.

fast

A transistor switch can operate _____ than

⇨ a mechanical switch.

faster

For a transistor to operate like a switch, it must be turned *ON* (full conduction) or turned *OFF* (no conduction). When a transistor is _____, we have maximum current flow; when it is

⇨ _____ we have minimum current flow.

ON

OFF

285

If a transistor is _____, we have maximum current flow.

▽

ON

A transistor is operating in the saturation region when maximum current is flowing through it. Such a transistor is in the _____ state.

▽

ON (conducting)

When a transistor switch is in the ON state, it is operating in the s_____ region.

▽

saturation

The _____ region of a transistor is reached by increasing the current through it to maximum.

▽

saturation

When a transistor is in the ON state, _____ current will flow and the transistor will operate in the _____ region.

▽

maximum
saturation

If the transistor is in the _____ state, we have minimum current flow.

▽

OFF (non-conducting)

A transistor is operating in the cutoff region when minimum current is flowing through it. Such a transistor is in the _____ state.

▽

OFF (non-conducting)

When a transistor is in the OFF state, it is operating in the c_____ region.

The _____ region of a transistor is reached by decreasing the current through it to a minimum.

When a transistor is in the OFF state, _____ current will flow, and the transistor will operate in the _____ region.

The transistor, when *used* as a switch, operates at two levels:
(1) _____ for maximum current flow
(2) _____ for minimum current flow

The two levels (ON, OFF) that will be maintained by the transistor switch are determined by the *steady-state* characteristics. The ON and OFF levels of a transistor switch are determined by the s_____-s_____ characteristics.

Since the transistor at the ON level is at saturation and at the OFF level is at cutoff, we can say that the saturation and cutoff points are determined by the _____-_____ characteristics.

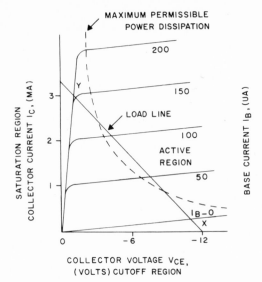

MAXIMUM PERMISSIBLE
POWER DISSIPATION

SATURATION REGION
COLLECTOR CURRENT I_C, (MA)

BASE CURRENT I_B, (UA)

200

150

LOAD LINE

100

ACTIVE
REGION

50

I_B-0

X

Y

3

2

1

0   −6   −12

COLLECTOR VOLTAGE V_{CE},
(VOLTS) CUTOFF REGION

NOTE:

THE LOADLINE IS SHOWN PASSING THROUGH THE
AREA BEYOND THE MAXIMUM PERMISSIBLE POWER
DISSIPATION CURVE. FOR NORMAL AMPLIFIER OPERATION
OF A TRANSISTOR THIS IS UNDESIRABLE. IN SWITCHING
CIRCUITS HOWEVER, THE EXCURSION OF THE COLLECTOR
CURRENT THROUGH THIS AREA IS VERY RAPID, AND
THE AVERAGE POWER DISSIPATED WITHIN THE TRAN-
SISTOR FALLS WITHIN THE ACCEPTABLE MAXIMUM
LIMITATIONS.

TRANSISTOR OUTPUT CHARACTERISTIC CURVES, SWITCHING
APPLICATION FOR COMMON EMITTER CONFIGURATION

Figure 2

The s _____ -s _____ levels are determined by two
points, *X* and *Y,* in Figure 2, the OFF and ON points,
⟁ respectively.

steady-state

In order to achieve the correct _____ - _____ levels,
⟁ the transistor must be properly biased.

steady-state

288

With proper _____ applied to a transistor, the steady states can be attained. Since in a transistor switch there are two steady-state levels necessary, there will be _____ (how many?) necessary

▽ bias conditions.

bias

two

A transistor is active or conducting (ON) when the emitter-base junction is _____ biased, and

▽ the collector-base junction is _____ biased.

forward

reverse

The transistor is inactive (OFF) when both junctions

▽ are _____ biased.

reverse

If the transistor is in the inactive (OFF) state it can be turned on by applying a large signal pulse which

▽ would _____ bias the emitter-base junction.

forward

This large signal pulse causes the transistor to jump

▽ from one _____-_____ level to another.

steady-state

The two levels that will be maintained by the transistor switch are determined by the _____-_____ characteristics. These two levels are _____

▽ and _____.

steady-state

saturation⎫
  cutoff⎬ *(either order)*

A transistor can be switched from cutoff (OFF) to saturation (ON) by application of a _____ (large, small) signal pulse.

large

A transistor can be switched from saturation (ON) to cutoff (OFF) by _____ (application, removal) of a large signal pulse, which will return the emitter-base junction to reverse bias.

removal

The switching speed of a transistor does not depend on mechanical parts, but the speed will depend on how fast the transistor goes from nonconduction to _____ and back to nonconduction.

conduction

The maximum switching speed of a transistor switch is determined by the cutoff frequency. State the definition of cutoff frequency ($f\alpha$).

the frequency at which the current gain of the transistor drops three db from maximum gain

The s_____ s_____ of a transistor is the ability of the transistor to conduct and cut off in rapid succession.

switching speed

Transient characteristics of a transistor determine the cutoff frequency which in turn determines the s_____ s_____ of the transistor. In order to compute the switching speed of a transistor, the t_____ c_____ must be known. (Normally all data of this type is supplied by the manufacturer.)

switching speed
transient characteristics

290

The _____ characteristics determine the _____ frequency of a transistor.

transient
cutoff (fα)

Transient characteristics determine cutoff frequency which determines _____.

switching
speed

_____ determine cutoff frequency which determines _____.

Transient characteristics
switching speed

_____ determine _____ which determines the switching speed of a transistor.

Transient characteristics
cutoff frequency (fα)

The _____ is therefore dependent on the transient characteristics.

switching
speed

The maximum switching speed at which a transistor may be driven is determined by the _____.

transient characteristics

A transistor has two sets of characteristics that are important:
(1) steady-state characteristics, and
(2) _____ characteristics.

transient (cutoff frequency
[fα])

291

The two areas to be investigated when discussing transistor switches are:

(1) _____-_____ (discrete levels that the transistor is to maintain), and

(2) _____ (speed that the transistor is to operate).

⬦

(1) steady-state characteristics
(2) transient characteristics

set **2** **OPERATION OF A TRANSISTOR SWITCH**

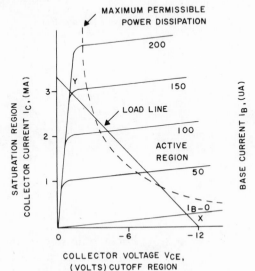

NOTE:

THE LOADLINE IS SHOWN PASSING THROUGH THE AREA BEYOND THE MAXIMUM PERMISSIBLE POWER DISSIPATION CURVE. FOR NORMAL AMPLIFIER OPERATION OF A TRANSISTOR THIS IS UNDESIRABLE. IN SWITCHING CIRCUITS HOWEVER, THE EXCURSION OF THE COLLECTOR CURRENT THROUGH THIS AREA IS VERY RAPID, AND THE AVERAGE POWER DISSIPATED WITHIN THE TRANSISTOR FALLS WITHIN THE ACCEPTABLE MAXIMUM LIMITATIONS.

TRANSISTOR OUTPUT CHARACTERISTIC CURVES, SWITCHING APPLICATION FOR COMMON EMITTER CONFIGURATION

Figure 2

In Figure 2, the *nonlinear* operating regions are the cutoff region and the saturation region. Once the steady-state characteristics of a transistor switch are determined, we know the limits of the n

⟳   operating regions.

nonlinear

293

The _____ operating regions of a transistor are determined by the steady-state characteristics of the transistor.

nonlinear

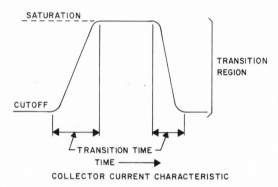

Figure 3

For a transistor to be used as a switch it must be properly biased so that a large signal pulse will cause it to operate in the _____ regions. (See Figure 3.)

nonlinear

In large signal operation, a rectangular input signal drives the transistor from cutoff to saturation and back to cutoff. The transistor _____ (has, has not) operated in the nonlinear region.

has

_____ operation results in an output waveform which may differ considerably from the input waveform.

nonlinear

A voltage which undergoes an instantaneous change in amplitude from one constant level to another is called a *unit step voltage*. A _____ is formed when a voltage rises instantaneously in the positive ⟁ direction.

unit step voltage

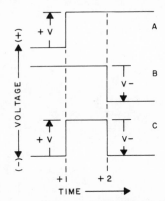

UNIT STEP VOLTAGE WAVEFORMS SHOWING
THE FORMATION OF A PULSE

Figure 4

A _____ is formed when a voltage rises instantaneously in the negative direction. (See Figure ⟁ 4B.)

unit step voltage

A voltage which undergoes a(n) _____ change in amplitude from one constant level to another in either a positive or negative direction, is ⟁ called a unit step voltage. (See Figure 4C.)

instantaneous

In pulse and switching circuit application, when the unit step voltage is the applied signal, it is usually of sufficient magnitude to cause the transistor to change from the ON state to the _____ ⟁ state or vice versa.

OFF

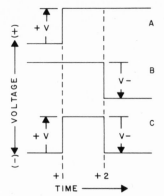

UNIT STEP VOLTAGE WAVEFORMS SHOWING
THE FORMATION OF A PULSE

Figure 4

Refer to Figure 4A. At time T_1 the voltage level is increased by the magnitude V. This is a unit _____ which increased in the positive direction.

step voltage

Keep in mind that the voltage level does not necessarily increase from zero to a positive voltage. If the initial voltage level were at a negative potential and then changed to zero, a positive unit step voltage would be involved.

Proceed to next frame.

Refer to Figure 4B. At time T_2, the voltage level is decreased by the magnitude V. This is a _____ which decreased in the negative direction.

unit step voltage

Refer to Figure 4C. At time $T_2 - T_1$, a constant voltage level is established. At time T_1, the voltage level _____ (increased, decreased, did not change). At time T_2, the voltage _____ (increased, decreased, did not change).

increased
decreased

The rectangular pulse of Figure 4C has two _____ voltages.

unit step

A voltage which undergoes an instantaneous change in amplitude from one constant level to another is called a _____.

unit step voltage

In order for a transistor to operate as a switch it must be driven by a large input signal. This large signal causes the transistor to operate from the cutoff region to the _____ region.

saturation

Such a circuit may be compared to an overdriven amplifier, which is designed for _____ (linear, nonlinear) operation.

nonlinear

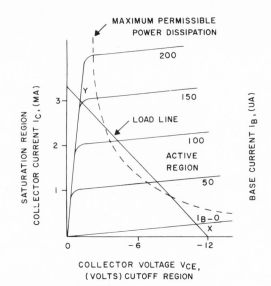

TRANSISTOR OUTPUT CHARACTERISTIC CURVES, SWITCHING APPLICATION FOR COMMON EMITTER CONFIGURATION

Figure 2

The collector-emitter (CE) output characteristics of a typical P-N-P transistor are shown in Figure 2. The characteristics of the transistor are arranged in three regions: ＿＿＿＿＿＿＿, ＿＿＿＿＿＿＿, and ＿＿＿＿＿＿＿.

⇨

cutoff
active
saturation

298

The quiescent state can be said to exist when the transistor switch is in the cutoff or saturation region with no input signal present. A multivibrator, for example, has two transistors — one at cutoff and one in saturation. An input pulse will reverse this condition.

▽ *Proceed to next frame.*

Quiescence is the state of a circuit with no signal applied. If a transistor switch is not conducting or is in full conduction with no signal applied it is said to
▽ be _____.

quiescent

A transistor switch which is cut off is said to be
▽ _____.

quiescent

A transistor switch which is at saturation could be
▽ _____.

quiescent

The _____ and _____ regions of a transistor switch are the quiescent regions if this is
▽ the state of the transistor with no input signal present.

cutoff
saturation

The *active* region of a transistor is the only region that will provide normal amplification gain. From the characteristic curve of Figure 2, state the limits
▽ of the active region. _____.

between points X and Y

The ____________ region of a transistor provides linear amplification. Would you say that this region is used when the transistor is operated as a switch? ____________.

active
The transistor goes through the active region, but has its limits of operation at cutoff and saturation.

A transistor amplifier which operates only in the ____________ region, has an output which is linear (not distorted).

active

Usually, when the transistor is used as a switch, the active region is known as the transient region. The ____________ region of a transistor switch is the same as the active region of a transistor amplifier.

transient

A transistor switch operates from the OFF to the ON state by passing through the ____________ region.

transient

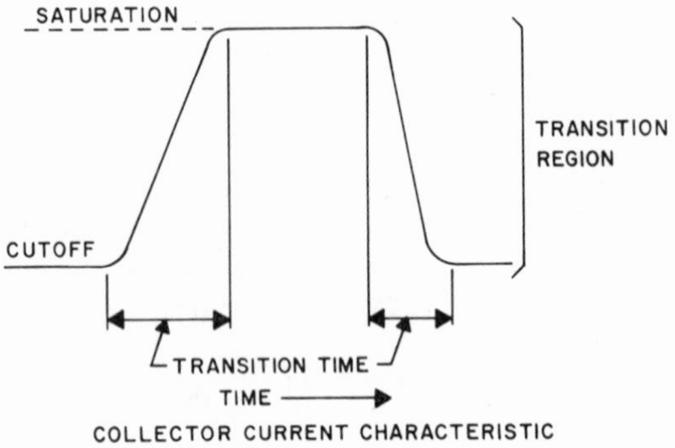

Figure 3

A large signal pulse applied to the input of a transistor switch circuit causes the transistor to operate from the cutoff region, through the _____ region, to the saturation region and back to cutoff. ⟳ (See Figure 3.)

transient

Starting at cutoff, describe the path of operation for a transistor switch, naming each region.

⟳ _____

_____

from cutoff, through transient, to saturation, back through transient, to cutoff

301

PULSE AND SWITCHING CIRCUITS

set

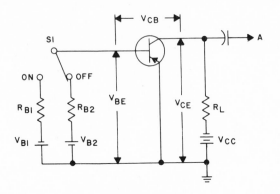

TRANSISTOR SWITCHING CIRCUIT
COMMON EMITTER CONFIGURATION

Figure 5

Figure 5 represents a *common-emitter* transistor switching circuit. In this circuit the _____ of the transistor is connected to ground.

emitter

When V_{B1} is applied to the base, the emitter-base junction will be biased in the _____ direction.

forward

V_{B2} applied to the base will bias the emitter-base junction in the _____ direction.

reverse

With S1 in the OFF position, battery voltage, _____, is applied to the base, and the emitter-base junction is _____ biased.

V_{B2}
reverse

302

⇩ The collector-base junction is _____ biased.

reverse

⇩ With the emitter-base and collector-base junctions reverse biased, the current through the collector is equal to _____.

zero

⇩ Current through R_L is equal to _____.

zero

⇩ The voltage across the collector and emitter, V_{CE}, is equal to _____.

V_{CC}

⇩ The transistor is operating in the _____ region.

cutoff

⇩ With S1 in the ON position, the emitter-base junction is _____ biased.

forward

⇩ What type of bias do you think is on the collector base junction? _____.

If you said forward bias, you are correct and probably a genius. The following frames will show you how the collector-base junction becomes forward biased.

⇩ With S1 in the ON position, the collector current is _____ (maximum, minimum).

maximum (high)

303

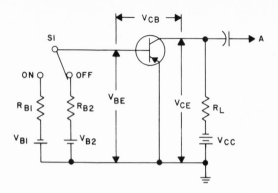

TRANSISTOR SWITCHING CIRCUIT
COMMON EMITTER CONFIGURATION

Figure 5

▽ The current through R_L is _____.

maximum (high)

▽ The voltage drop across R_L would be _____.

maximum (high)

▽ Therefore, the collector voltage, V_{CE}, is _____.

at minimum (low), (zero)

When S1 was in the OFF position, V_{CE} was equal to

▽ _____.

V_{CC} (or maximum in negative direction)

When S1 was thrown from the OFF to the ON position, the voltage at the collector changed to become

▽ more _____ (positive, negative).

positive

304

A positive going voltage at the collector will
_____ bias the collector-base junction.

forward

With S1 in the ON position, the emitter-base junction
is _____ biased and the collector-base junction is _____ biased.

forward
forward

The transistor is operating in the _____
(cutoff, transient, saturation) region with S1 in the
ON position.

saturation

Now suppose we operate S1 in a sequence from OFF
to ON to OFF. What type of a waveform would you
expect at point *A*? (Indicate voltages.)

For a common-base configuration, the transient characteristics are better than in the common-emitter configuration. Since the transient characteristics are good,
it is best used in _____ (high, low) speed
transistor switching circuits.

high

305

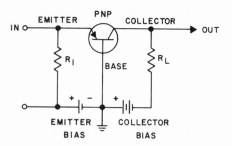

COMMON BASE CONFIGURATION

Figure 6

A positive voltage applied to the input of the common-base configuration in Figure 6, will _____ bias the emitter-base junction. (The quiescent state is in the cutoff region.)

forward

The collector will show a _____ (positive, negative) unit step voltage. (See Figure 6.)

positive

With the common-base configuration there _____ (will, will not) be a phase inversion.

will not

What kind of an output would there be if a negative voltage were applied to the input? (See Figure 6.) _____.

no output (collector voltage remains negative)

A _____-_____ transistor in a common-base configuration acts as a switch for positive pulses. How can a common-base configuration act as a switch to pass negative pulses? _____.

P-N-P
by using an N-P-N transistor

306

set **4**

TRANSISTOR OUTPUT PULSE
CHARACTERISTICS

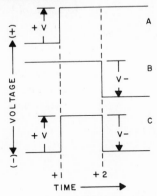

UNIT STEP VOLTAGE WAVEFORMS SHOWING
THE FORMATION OF A PULSE

Figure 4

In large signal operation, a rectangular input signal drives the transistor switch from cutoff to saturation and back to cutoff. This rectangular input signal is made up of a _____ and _____ unit step voltage. (See Figure 4.)

positive
negative

A rectangular input signal is made up of a positive and negative _____.

unit step voltage

In large signal operation, the transistor acts as an overdriven amplifier with resultant changes in the conduction state. The transistor is therefore driven from cutoff to _____ and back to _____.

saturation
cutoff

307

A distorted output current pulse will result because a transistor cannot respond instantaneously to a change in signal level. The output signal _____ (is, is not) identical in all respects to the input signal.

is not

Distortion in the _____ can be noted in the four basic pulse characteristics: rise time, pulse time, storage time, and fall time.

output pulse (output signal)

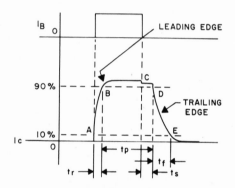

CURRENT PULSE CHARACTERISTICS, SWITCHING CIRCUIT

Figure 7

The rise time, t_r (also referred to as build-up time or turn-on time) is the time required for the *leading edge* of the pulse to increase in amplitude from 10 to 90 percent of its maximum value. (Points A and B, Figure 7.) The rise time is associated with the _____ edge of a pulse.

leading

The rise time of a pulse is that portion on the _____ edge between 10 and 90 percent of its maximum amplitude.

leading

308

The pulse characteristic of that portion of the leading edge which lies between 10 to 90 percent of the maximum amplitude is called _____.

rise time

The time required for the leading edge of a pulse to increase in amplitude from _____ to _____ percent of its maximum value is called rise time (t_r).

10
90

The symbol for rise time is _____.

t_r

The rise time is associated with the _____ _____ of a pulse and is defined as _____ (use own words).

leading edge
time required to go from 10 to 90 percent of maximum amplitude

The slope of the leading edge of the output current pulse for a transistor is a result of the *nonlinear* characteristics and the *circuit configuration* for the transistor. The rise time is dependent upon the _____ characteristics and the _____ configuration of the transistor.

nonlinear
circuit

The slope of the leading edge of the output current pulse is dependent upon the _____ characteristics and circuit configuration of the transistor.

nonlinear

309

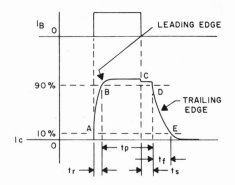

CURRENT PULSE CHARACTERISTICS, SWITCHING CIRCUIT

Figure 7

The _____ and circuit _____ of a transistor are contributing factors in the determination of rise time.

↕

nonlinear characteristics
configuration

Overdriving the transistor will result in decreasing the rise time. The _____ can be decreased by applying a large input signal that overdrives the transistor.

↕

rise time

Reduction of the rise time can be accomplished by _____ (complete the sentence).

↕

overdriving the transistor
or applying a large input
signal

Although the rise time can be _____ (increased, decreased) by overdriving the transistor, a disadvantage is the lengthening of the storage time and the fall time. (See Figure 7.)

↕

decreased

310

If the output pulse is much longer in duration than the input signal, the transistor is probably being

▽ _____.

overdriven

The pulse time (t_p), or duration time, is the length of time that the pulse remains at or near its maximum value. In Figure 7, the pulse time is between points

▽ _____ and _____.

B
D

The pulse time is measured from the point on the leading edge (B) where the amplitude of the pulse has reached _____ percent of its maximum value to the point on the trailing edge where the amplitude has fallen to _____ percent of its

▽ maximum value (D).

90
90

▽ The symbol for pulse time is _____.

t_p

In Figure 7, when the input current (I_B) goes to zero the output current (I_C) _____ (does,

▽ does not) immediately fall to zero.

does not

Right after the input current (I_B) is cut off, the output current (I_C) remains at an approximate level indicated by points _____ and _____

▽ in Figure 7.

C
D

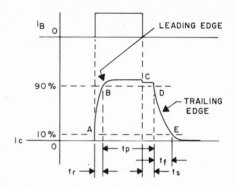

CURRENT PULSE CHARACTERISTICS, SWITCHING CIRCUIT

Figure 7

The output pulse characteristic which occurs immediately after the input signal is cut off to a point on the trailing edge where the amplitude has fallen to 90 percent of its maximum value is called *storage time* (t_s). The _____ of I_C in Figure 7 is indicated by points C and D.

The point on the output pulse where the input signal was cut off, and the point where the collector current has been reduced to 90 percent of its maximum value determines the _____.

Storage time results from the injected *minority carriers* being in the base and collector regions at the moment when the input is cut off. Residual current in the transistor resulting from injected _____ in the base and collector regions causes storage time.

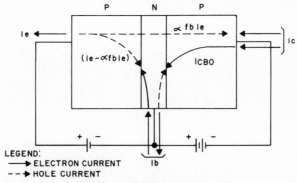

CURRENT FLOW IN A PNP TRANSISTOR

Figure 8

Refer to Figure 8 _____ (Holes, Electrons) constitute the main current carriers through a P-N-P transistor.

▽

Holes

The emitter-base junction of the transistor is _____ biased.

▽

forward

▽ The collector-base junction is _____ biased.

reverse

When the transistor is conducting, the minority carriers in the *base* region are _____ (holes, electrons).

▽

holes

When the transistor is conducting, the minority carriers in the collector region would be _____ (holes, electrons).

▽

electrons

313

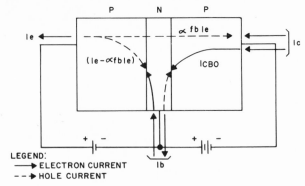

CURRENT FLOW IN A PNP TRANSISTOR

Figure 8

In this case, electron flow for the minority carriers would be from the _____ to the _____.

collector
base

The instant the transistor is cut off (emitter-base junction reverse bias) there would be an excess of _____ (electrons, holes) in the collector region and an excess of _____ (electrons, holes) in the base region. This is called minority carrier storage.

electrons
holes

Storage time results from injected _____ carriers being in the base and collector regions of the transistor at the moment when the input is cut off.

minority

Under this condition the collector current would _____ for a short period of time until equilibrium occurs.

flow (continue)

314

When the input current, I_B, is cut off, the output current, I_C, continues to flow for a short period of time because of _____ storage.

minority carrier

If a collector load resistor were in the circuit of Figure 8, and the emitter-base junction were forward biased, current flow through the resistor would cause a _____ polarity at the bottom and a _____ polarity at the top of the resistor.

negative
positive

If a collector load resistor were in the circuit, the polarity across the resistor at the first instant after the emitter base junction was reversed biased, would be _____ at the bottom and _____ at the top.

negative
positive

In both these cases, electron flow was in the _____ (same, opposite) direction.

same

In both cases the polarity of the voltage drop across the resistor was _____. (The level of I_C taken across the resistor during the storage time would be less because the main current flow has been cut off.)

the same

315

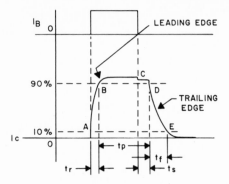

CURRENT PULSE CHARACTERISTICS, SWITCHING CIRCUIT

Figure 7

The storage time of the output pulse in Figure 7 lies
☟ between points _____ and _____.

C
D

The storage time will be _____ (increased,
decreased) if a transistor switch were operated deep
☟ in the saturated region.

increased

For high speed switching _____ (long,
☟ short) storage time is desirable.

short

The _____ would be minimized if the transistor switch were operated in the transient (active)
☟ region.

storage time

The length of the _____ is essentially governed by the degree of saturation into which the tran-
☟ sistor is driven and the time spent in saturation.

storage time

316

For high speed switching storage time is
⬦ _____ (desirable, undesirable).

undesirable

Minority carrier storage (storage time) may be minimized by switching the transistor from its OFF state
⬦ to a point in the _____ region.

active (transient)

Storage time results from the injected _____
_____ being in the base and collector re-
⬦ gions at the moment the input is cut off.

minority carriers

Fall or *decay* time, t_f, is that portion of the trailing
edge of a pulse lying between 90 and 10 percent of
its maximum amplitude. In Figure 7, the portion of
the pulse between D and E is the _____
⬦ _____.

fall time (decay time)

The time required for the trailing edge of a pulse to
decrease in amplitude from 90 to 10 percent of its
⬦ maximum value is called _____.

fall time (decay time)

The fall time of a pulse is that portion on the
_____ edge between _____ and
⬦ _____ percent of its maximum amplitude.

trailing
90
10

317

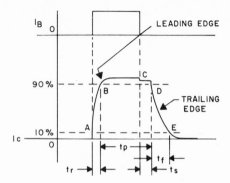

CURRENT PULSE CHARACTERISTICS, SWITCHING CIRCUIT

Figure 7

In Figure 7, the fall time lies between points
⬦ _____ and _____.

D

E

⬦ The symbol for fall time is _____.

t_f

The slope of the trailing edge of the output current
pulse for a transistor is a result of the *nonlinear characteristics* and *circuit configuration* for the transistor.
The rise time also is dependent upon the
_____ characteristics and _____
⬦ configuration of the transistor.

nonlinear
circuit

The slope of the trailing edge of the output current
pulse is dependent upon the _____ and
⬦ _____ of the transistor.

nonlinear characteristics
circuit configuration

318

That portion of a pulse on the *leading* edge between 10 and 90 percent of its maximum amplitude is the ⟁ _____ time.

rise

The length of time that the output pulse remains at or near its maximum value is the _____ ⟁ time (t_p).

pulse

The output pulse time may be decreased by:
(1) decreasing the input pulse duration;
(2) _____ (increasing, decreasing) the stor-
⟁ age time.

decreasing

The output pulse characteristic which occurs from the moment the input signal is cut off to a point on the trailing edge where the amplitude has fallen to 90 percent of its maximum value is called
⟁ _____ time.

storage

The pulse characteristic of that portion of the trailing edge which lies between 90 and 10 percent of the
⟁ maximum amplitude is called _____ time.

fall

The four basic output pulse characteristics are:
(1) _____ time   (3) _____ time
⟁ (2) _____ time   (4) _____ time

(1) rise
(2) pulse
(3) storage
(4) fall

set 5

HIGH SPEED SWITCHING

The storage time of an output pulse will be ______________ (increased, decreased) if a transistor switch were operated deep in the saturation region.

increased

For high speed switching, ______________ (long, short) storage time is desirable.

short

The length of the ______________ time is essentially governed by the degree of saturation into which the transistor is driven and the time spent in saturation.

storage

A transistor which is driven into saturation may introduce ______________ (desirable, undesirable) effects on the output waveform.

undesirable

The ______________ time would be minimized if the transistor switch were operated in the transient (active) region.

storage

Storage time may be minimized by switching the transistor to a point in the ______________ region.

transient (or active)

Another way to increase the frequency response (switching speed) of a transistor switch is to decrease the *rise* time. The _____ time can be decreased by applying a high level input signal ("turn on" current).

⟁ *rise*

A high level input signal will _____ the rise time.

⟁ *decrease*

This high level signal will be a negative unit step voltage for a P-N-P and a positive unit step voltage for an N-P-N in common-emitter switch configurations.

⟁ *Proceed to next frame.*

The frequency response may be improved by decreasing the *fall* time. The _____ time can be decreased by applying a high level signal to drive the transistor into cutoff ("turn off" current).

⟁ *fall*

⟁ A high level signal will _____ the fall time.

decrease

This high level signal must be a positive unit step voltage for a P-N-P or a negative unit step voltage for an N-P-N, common-emitter switch configuration.

⟁ *Proceed to next frame.*

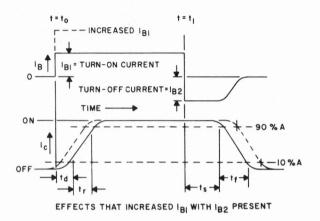

Figure 9

Refer to Figure 9. At time zero, $t = t_o$; if I_B were increased to I_{B1}, t_r would be _____.

decreased

At this point a new factor is introduced; that is, the output pulse delay time (t_d). It has little bearing on the frequency response.

Proceed to next frame.

If the transistor is driven hard into cutoff, by applying a current (I_{B2}) in the reverse direction, the fall time, t_f, at $t = t_1$ will be _____. (See Figure 9.)

decreased

In order to have a high speed transistor switch, it is necessary to decrease the _____ time, _____ time, and _____ time.

rise
storage
fall
(any order)

322

For a transistor switch to have a high repetition rate, the rise time, storage time, and fall time must be

⇦ _____.

short

Three transistor output pulse characteristics which are important when talking about high switching speeds are _____ time, _____ time, and _____ time.

⇦

rise
storage
fall

A high level input signal will _____ the storage time.

⇦

increase

It is therefore necessary to have a configuration that will allow the transistor to operate at the fastest speed possible. One method to achieve this is called *cutoff* and *saturation clamping.*

⇦ *Proceed to next frame.*

_____ and saturation clamping is one method used which enables a transistor to operate at a fast repetition rate.

⇦

Cutoff

To operate a transistor at high switching speeds, a method called _____ and _____ clamping may be employed.

⇦

cutoff
saturation

323

A switch configuration which uses cutoff and saturation clamping will operate at ＿＿＿＿＿＿ (higher, lower) switching speeds on any transistor.

higher

＿＿＿＿＿＿ and ＿＿＿＿＿＿ clamping will allow the transistor switch to be operated by high level input signals but prevents it from going into saturation.

Cutoff
saturation

If the transistor switch cannot operate in the saturation region then it must be operated in the ＿＿＿＿＿＿ region.

active (transient)

A transistor switch which can only operate in the ＿＿＿＿＿＿ region and cutoff region is called a nonsaturated transistor.

active (or transient)

A ＿＿＿＿＿＿ transistor operates only in the active region and cutoff region.

nonsaturated

The output pulse characteristic that would be minimized if the transistor switch were operated only in the active region and cutoff region is ＿＿＿＿＿＿ time, since it depends on how far into saturation the operation extends.

storage

A nonsaturated transistor which is operated by a large input signal will have a _____ (fast, slow) switching speed.

fast

The output pulse characteristics which are shortened when a nonsaturated transistor is operated by a large input signal are:
(1) _____ time   (2) _____ time
(3) _____ time

rise
storage
fall
(any order)

It is appropriate at this time to point out that the storage time will have the greatest decrease. The storage time will therefore have the greatest over-all effect on the switching speed.

HIGH SPEED SWITCHING WITH CUTOFF AND SATURATION CLAMPING

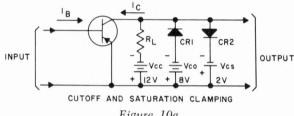

CUTOFF AND SATURATION CLAMPING

Figure 10a

Refer to Figure 10a. A large signal input under normal conditions (that is, without clamping diodes CR1 and CR2, and their respective bias batteries V_{co} *and* V_{cs}) will drive the transistor into _____.

▽

saturation

The voltage at the collector would be _____ (minimum, maximum).

▽

minimum

If the input signal is taken away, the transistor is in the _____ region.

▽

cutoff

▽ The voltage at the collector is now _____.

− 12 volts (or at maximum in the negative direction)

326

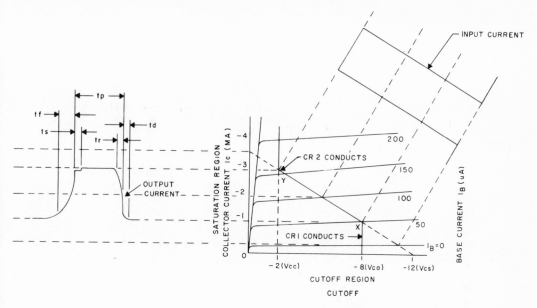

Figure 10b

The output characteristics are shown in Figure 10b. The output pulse has been driven from _____ to _____ and back to _____.

▽

cutoff
saturation
cutoff

Assume that CR1 and its bias battery, V_{co}, are now in the circuit of Figure 10a. Initially (without CR1 in the circuit), the potential at cutoff on the collector was about _____ volts.

▽

-12

As soon as clamping diode CR1 with its bias battery was placed in the circuit, the potential across the diode was _____ volts at the cathode and _____ volts at the plate.

▽

-12
-8

The polarity at the cathode is _____ (positive, negative) with respect to the polarity at the plate of CR1.

negative

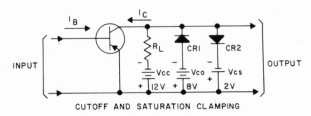

INPUT   OUTPUT

CUTOFF AND SATURATION CLAMPING

Figure 10a

Clamping diode, CR1, becomes _____ (forward, reverse) biased and begins to conduct.

forward

Current is now flowing from V_{cc}, through R_L, through CR1 to V_{cc}. The polarity of the voltage across R_L is _____ at the bottom and _____ at the top.

negative
positive

The voltage drop across R_L is _____ volts. $(V_{cc} - V_{co})$

4

Therefore, the voltage at the collector is _____ volts.

− 8

Now let us place CR2 and its bias battery, V_{cs}, in the circuit of Figure 10a. The potential on the diode is _____ volts at the plate and _____ volts at the cathode with no signal applied to the base.

− 8
− 2

328

The polarity at the plate with respect to the polarity at the cathode of CR2 is _____ (negative, positive).

negative

Clamping diode, CR2, becomes _____ (forward, reverse) biased and will not conduct.

reversed

With a large input signal, the transistor will conduct. The voltage at the collector will go from _____ to −2 volts.

− 8

As the collector voltage tries to go more positive than −2 volts, CR2 will become _____ (forward, reverse) biased.

forward

With CR2 forward biased, it will _____ (conduct, remain at the cutoff).

conduct

Therefore, the voltage at the collector, with a large signal input, can never go more positive than _____ volts.

− 2

With a large signal input, once the voltage goes more positive than −8 volts, CR1 would be _____ (forward, reverse) biased.

reverse

CR1 would be _____ (conducting, cutoff).

cutoff

329

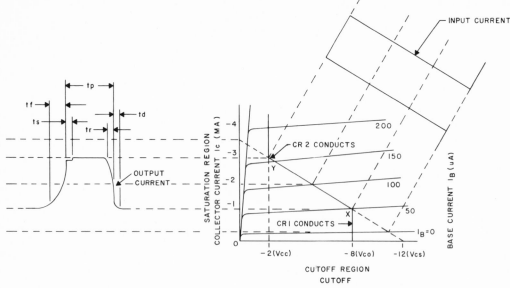

Figure 10b

Refer to Figure 10b. Looking at the characteristic curves for the transistor configuration of Figure 10b, we see that the collector voltage varies from

☛ _____ volts to _____ volts.

− 8
− 2
(either order)

With the transistor at cutoff, _____ is con-
☛ ducting. (See Figure 10b.)

CR1

With the collector voltage between −8 volts and −2
☛ volts CR1 is _____.

cutoff

The collector voltage will be held at −2 volts with
a large signal input. At −2 volts (collector voltage),
☛ _____ is conducting.

CR2

The transistor is operating only in the _____ region and cutoff region.

active (or transient)

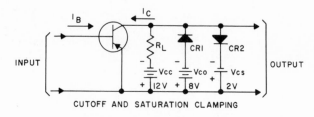

CUTOFF AND SATURATION CLAMPING

Figure 10a

Is it possible for the transistor to operate in the saturation region with the configuration shown in Figure 10a? _____.

No. If your answer was yes you better review this section.

Refer to Figures 10a and b. The transistor will not conduct until I_b reaches a value of _____ μA.

50

At 50 μA CR1 becomes _____ biased to allow collector current to flow.

reverse

When I_B reaches 50 μA, collector current will immediately flow at about _____ ma.

1

This sudden increase in collector current will _____ (increase, decrease) the rise time, t_r.

decrease

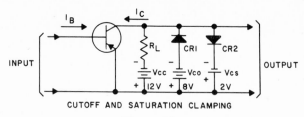

CUTOFF AND SATURATION CLAMPING

Figure 10a

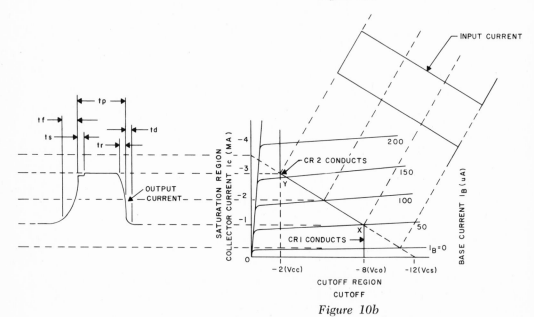

Figure 10b

When I_B reaches 150 μA, the collector current will be at about _____ ma.

3

For any further increase in I_B, you will have an increase in I_C but V_{ce} will remain at _____ volts.

— 2 volts

The vertical extension of the load line from point Y represents the *zero resistance load line* of forward biased diode CR2.

Proceed to next frame.

332

When the driving current, I_B, is reduced to 50 μA, the collector current, I_C, falls rapidly to point Y along the _____ resistance load line. (See Figure 10b.)

zero

From point Y the collector current will then follow the normal load line toward point _____.

X

A further decrease in I_B, to zero, has no effect on the collector potential, which will remain fixed at _____ volts.

− 8

There is a sudden _____ in collector current as soon as collector current reaches point X on the load line.

decrease

This sudden decrease will cause the fall time, t_f to _____.

decrease

To sum it up, cutoff and saturation clamping will _____ the:
(1) rise time (2) storage time (3) fall time

decrease

_____ and _____ clamping will allow a transistor to operate at higher switching speeds.

Saturation
cutoff

set 7

MULTIVIBRATORS: FREE-RUNNING (ASTABLE)

A *multivibrator* is a circuit usually containing two transistors in which the transistors conduct alternately. A circuit containing two transistors in which one conducts when the other is cut off and vice versa is called a(n) ______________.

multivibrator

A typical multivibrator contains ______________ transistors.

two

When one transistor is conducting the other is ______________.

cut off (not conducting)

In a *free-running* (astable) multivibrator no input signal is required to change the state of the transistors. A multivibrator which requires no input signals is ______________.

free-running (astable)

Since *oscillations* occur by the changing of states in a free-running multivibrator, this circuit is essentially a type of ______________.

oscillator

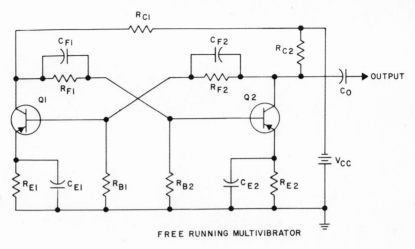

FREE RUNNING MULTIVIBRATOR

Figure 11

Figure 11 is a multivibrator containing two P-N-P transistors which are resistance-capacitance (RC) coupled and have common emitters.

↶ *Proceed to the next frame.*

The transistors in the multivibrator in Figure 11 are _____ - _____ coupled.

resistance-capacitance
(RC)

The transistors in this multivibrator circuit have common _____.

emitters

In this multivibrator circuit, the *output* (collector) of the first transistor is coupled to the *input* (base) of the second transistor. The output of the second transistor is coupled to the _____ (base) of the first transistor.

input

335

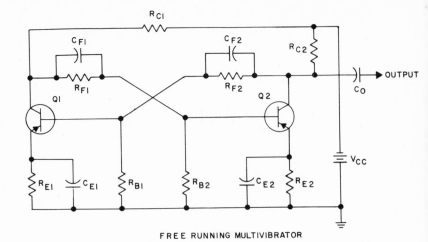

FREE RUNNING MULTIVIBRATOR

Figure 11

⊽ In this circuit, the inputs to the transistors are applied at the _____ and the outputs appear at the _____.

bases
collectors

⊽ The signal appearing at the collector of the first transistor is coupled to the _____ of the second transistor.

base (input)

⊽ The signal applied to the base of the first transistor is coupled from the _____ of the _____ transistor.

collector (output)
second

⊽ The transistors are _____ - _____ coupled.

resistance-capacitance
(RC)

When transistor Q1 is conducting, Q2 is

⇩ _____.

cut off (not conducting)

When no positive input signal is applied to the base of one of the transistors and V_{CC} causes this transistor to be forward biased, this transistor will be in the

⇩ _____ (conducting, nonconducting) state.

conducting

When a positive signal is applied to the base of a transistor, a bias in the _____ direction is

⇩ applied to the emitter-base junction.

reverse

A _____ (positive, negative) signal at the base of one of the transistors causes that transistor to

⇩ cut off.

positive

When no positive signal is applied to the base of a

⇩ transistor, that transistor will _____.

conduct

⇩ When Q2 is cutoff, _____ is conducting.

Q1

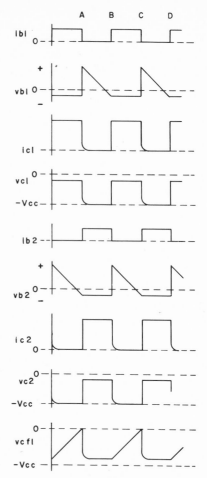

Figure 12   ASTABLE MULTIVIBRATOR WAVEFORMS

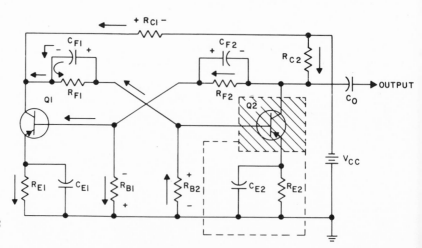

Figure 13

FREE RUNNING MULTIVIBRATOR
Q_1 CONDUCTING

In Figure 13, when Q1 is conducting, electron flow, indicated by the arrows, is _____ (into, out of) the collector.

▽

into

Refer to Figures 12 and 13. When Q1 conducts, electron current flowing into the collector of Q1 develops more voltage across resistor R_{C1}, making the voltage at the collector _____ (more, less) negative.

▽

less

The voltage at the collector of Q1, when Q1 is conducting, is equal to the difference between _____ and the voltage across R_{C1}.

▽

V_{CC}

At the instant Q1 begins to conduct, the voltage at the collector _____ (increases, decreases) in the positive direction or _____ in the negative direction.

▽

increases
decreases

A change in voltage at the collector of Q1 is coupled to the base of Q2 through the RC network, consisting of resistor _____, and capacitor _____.

▽

R_{F1}
C_{F1}

A positive change in voltage at the collector of Q1 is coupled to the _____ of transistor _____.

▽

base
Q2

339

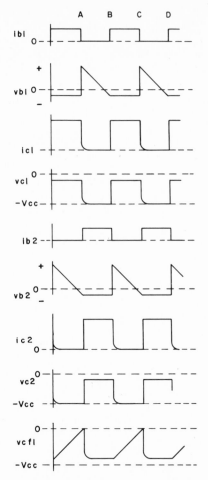

Figure 12   ASTABLE MULTIVIBRATOR WAVEFORMS

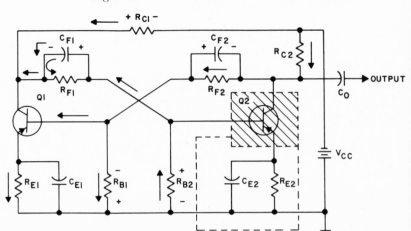

Figure 13

FREE RUNNING MULTIVIBRATOR
Q_1 CONDUCTING

A voltage change appearing at the base of Q2 appears across the resistor _____, since this resistor is connected between the base of Q2 and ground.

R_{B2}

The voltage appearing at the base of Q2 is always equal to the voltage across resistor _____.

R_{B2}

When Q1 goes into conduction, capacitor C_{F1} has already been charged according to the polarity indicated in Figures 12 and 13. Therefore, when the voltage at the collector of Q1 changes in the positive direction, capacitor C_{F1} is already _____.

charged

When Q1 goes into conduction, C_{F1} is _____.

charged

After Q1 begins to conduct, C_{F1} begins to _____.

discharge

Resistor R_{B2} is in the *discharge path* of capacitor C_{F1}. Q1 and R_{E1} are also in the _____ _____ of C_{F1}.

discharge path

Since R_{B2} is in the _____ of C_{F1}, the direction of electron current flow through R_{B2} is the same as the C_{F1} discharge current.

discharge path

341

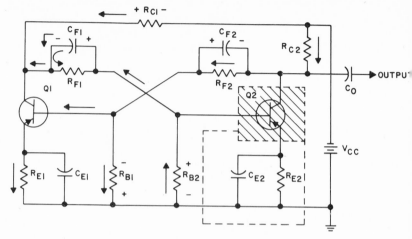

+ R_CI −

C_FI

R_FI

QI

C_F2

R_C2

R_F2

Q2

C_O

OUTPUT

V_CC

R_EI   C_EI   R_BI   R_B2   C_E2   R_E2

FREE RUNNING MULTIVIBRATOR
Q₁ CONDUCTING

Figure 13

As C_{F1} discharges, the direction of the discharge current flow is as indicated in Figure 13. This current flowing through R_{B2} creates a _____ voltage on the base of Q2.

positive (higher)

When transistor Q1 begins to conduct, capacitor C_{F1} begins to _____ (charge, discharge) and the voltage at the base of Q2 rapidly becomes more _____ because of the discharge current.

discharge
positive

When Q1 conducts the rise in voltage at its _____ is coupled to the base of Q2.

collector

A positive voltage at the base of Q2 creates a _____ bias on the emitter-base junction of Q2.

reverse

342

When Q1 begins to conduct, a reverse bias is applied to the emitter-base junction of _____ causing it to _____.

Q2
cut off

When Q2 is cut off, the voltage at the collector approaches _____ since there is no current flow through the transistor and consequently low current through R_{C2} and low voltage across R_{C2}.

V_{CC} (supply voltage)

Since the output is taken from the _____ of Q2, it also goes to V_{CC} when Q2 is cutoff.

collector

The V_{CC} (supply voltage) appearing at the collector of Q2 when it is cut off, is _____ (positive, negative) with respect to ground.

negative

The signal appearing at the collector of Q2 is coupled to the _____ of transistor _____.

base
Q1

The RC coupling circuit between the Q2 collector and the Q1 base consists of resistor _____ and capacitor _____.

R_{F2}
C_{F2}

Since the capacitor C_{F2} is *discharging* when Q2 is conducting, just before Q2 goes into cutoff C_{F2} is _____.

discharged

343

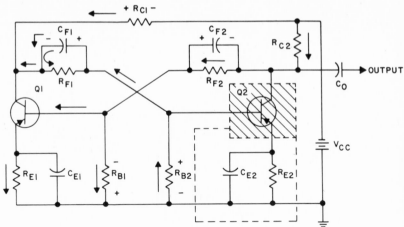

FREE RUNNING MULTIVIBRATOR
Q₁ CONDUCTING

Figure 13

As Q2 goes into cutoff, capacitor C_{F2} _____
▽   rapidly.

charges

The charge path for C_{F2} is through R_{B1}, V_{CC} and
▽ R_{C2} when transistor Q2 is _____.

cut off

Because of the low time constant determined by the
charge path, capacitor C_{F2} charges _____
▽   (rapidly, slowly).

rapidly

When Q2 is cut off, the current in R_{B1} is in the direction indicated by Figure 13. This creates a
▽   _____ voltage on the base of Q1.

*negative (low, forward
bias)*

344

As Q2 cuts off, C_{F2} _____ rapidly and a
_____ voltage appears at the base of Q1.

charges
negative (low)

When Q2 is cut off, the negative going voltage at the
base of Q1 creates an emitter-base bias in the
_____ direction.

forward

A forward bias on the base of Q1 drives it further
into the _____ (conducting, nonconducting)
state.

conducting

When Q1 is conducting and Q2 is cut off, the Q1
collector voltage is less _____ than the Q2
collector voltage.

negative (more positive)

At this point the Q1 base is _____ biased
and the Q2 base is _____ biased.

forward (negatively)
reverse (positively)

After Q1 begins to conduct and its collector voltage
rises, the capacitor _____ begins to discharge.

C_{F1}

The _____ path of C_{F1} includes Q1, R_{E1},
and R_{B2}.

discharge

345

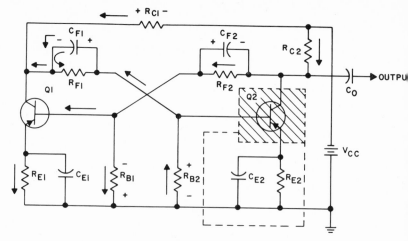

FREE RUNNING MULTIVIBRATOR
Q₁ CONDUCTING

Figure 13

The rate at which C_{F1} discharge is determined by the *time constant* of its discharge path. Thus, the change in current in this discharge path is determined by the

▽ _____ .

time constant

The change in current through R_{B2} is determined by

▽ the _____ of the discharge path.

time constant

As C_{F1} discharges the current through R_{B2}
_____ (increases, decreases) in the direc-

▽ tion shown in Figure 13.

decreases

This decrease in current causes the voltage across R_{B2}

▽ to _____ .

decrease

As the voltage across R_{B2} decreases, the voltage appearing at the base of Q2 becomes less _____ .

positive

As the voltage at the base of Q2 becomes less positive, the reverse bias _____ (increases, decreases).

decreases

As the capacitor C_{F1} discharges, the reverse bias on the base of Q2 _____ (increases, decreases).

decreases

The rate at which the reverse bias on the base of Q2 decreases depends on the _____ of the discharge circuit of C_{F1}.

time constant

As the capacitor C_{F1} discharges, the voltage across R_{B2} _____ .

decreases

As the voltage across the resistor R_{B2} decreases, the reverse bias on the Q2 base _____ .

decreases

When the reverse bias is decreased far enough, _____ bias is established.

forward

When sufficient forward bias is established on the base of Q2, this transistor will _____ .

conduct

347

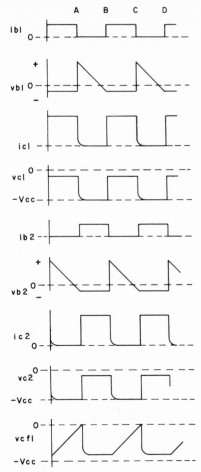

Figure 12   ASTABLE MULTIVIBRATOR WAVEFORMS

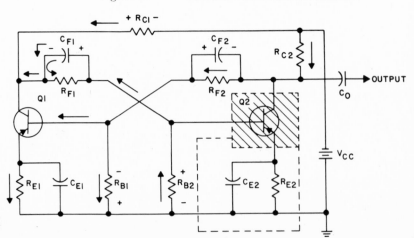

Figure 13

FREE RUNNING MULTIVIBRATOR
Q₁ CONDUCTING

When capacitor C_{F1} has discharged to a sufficient point, transistor Q2 will _____.

conduct

When transistor Q2 goes into conduction, its collector voltage _____ rapidly in the positive direction (becomes less negative).

increases

Also, when Q2 goes into conduction, capacitor C_{F1}, which has been discharging prior to this time, _____ rapidly as is shown by the waveforms in Figure 12.

charges

The output of the multivibrator circuit taken from the collector of Q2 _____ rapidly in the negative direction when Q2 goes into conduction.

decreases

The time at which Q2 conducts with its resultant negative collector voltage drop depends on the _____ of the discharge circuit of C_{F1}.

time constant

The drop in negative voltage at the Q2 collector is coupled to the _____ of transistor _____ where it appears as a positive voltage rise.

base
Q1

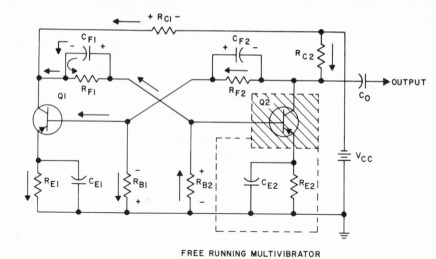

FREE RUNNING MULTIVIBRATOR
Q1 CONDUCTING

Figure 13

The negative decrease at the Q2 collector is coupled to the Q1 base through capacitor _____ and resistor _____.

C_{F2}
R_{F2}

The positive voltage rise coupled to the Q1 base biases transistor Q1 in the _____ direction.

reverse

The reverse bias on the Q1 base causes Q1 to _____.

cut off

Thus when Q2 goes into the _____ state, Q1 goes into the _____ state.

conduction
cutoff

350

This is accomplished by the coupling of the negative decrease in potential at the _____ of Q2 to the base of _____, where it appears as a positive rise and applies a reverse bias at the base of ⟁ _____, causing it to cut off.

collector
Q1
Q1

Capacitor C_{F2} then discharges, causing the voltage drop across the combination of C_{F2} and R_{F2} to _____ (increase, decrease) and consequently ⟁ the discharge current _____.

decrease
decreases

As the discharge current of C_{F2} decreases, the voltage ⟁ drop across R_{B1} _____.

decreases

As the voltage across the resistor R_{B1} decreases, the ⟁ voltage at the Q1 base _____.

decreases

A decrease in voltage at the base of Q1 causes the ⟁ reverse bias on Q1 to _____.

decrease

After the voltage at the base of Q1 has decreased to a sufficient level, Q1 will go back into the ⟁ _____ state.

conduction

351

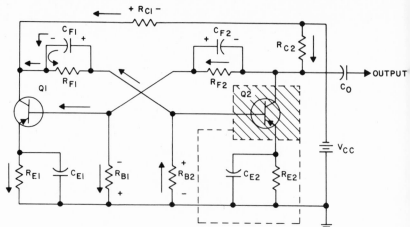

+ R_{CI} −

FREE RUNNING MULTIVIBRATOR
Q₁ CONDUCTING

Figure 13

When Q1 goes back into conduction, Q2 goes into
the _____ state.

cutoff

This switching continues for as long as the
_____ circuit is in operation.

multivibrator

When Q2 conducts, its collector voltage, which is the
output, is _____ than when Q2 is cut off.

*less negative (higher, more
positive)*

The waveform of the output is a square wave, the
voltage being less negative when transistor
_____ conducts and more negative when
transistor _____ conducts.

Q2
Q1

The waveform of the output of this multivibrator is

▽   a _____.

square wave

The square wave changes in voltage level each time

▽   the _____ change state.

transistors

The changing of states of the transistors is determined
by the RC time constant. Thus, the width of the out-

▽   put pulse is determined by the RC _____.

time constants

The RC _____ determines the _____

▽   of the output _____ waves.

time constant
width (frequency)
square

Stabilization is obtained for transistor Q1 with emitter
swamping resistor R_{E1}. Swamping resistor R_{E1} is used

▽   for the _____ of transistor Q1.

stabilization

▽ R_{E1} is a _____ resistor.

swamping (stabilizing)

Stabilization of Q2 is obtained through swamping

▽   resistor _____.

R_{E2}

Transistor _____ obtains stabilization from
R_{E1}, and R_{E2} provides stabilization for transistor

▽   _____.

Q1
Q2

353

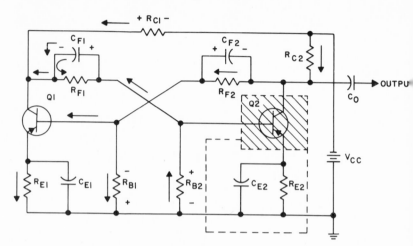

FREE RUNNING MULTIVIBRATOR
Q₁ CONDUCTING

Figure 13

R_{E2} is a _____ resistor and provides
_____ for transistor _____.

⇲

swamping
stabilization
Q2

Emitter capacitors C_{E1} and C_{E2} are *bypass* capacitors.
The capacitors C_{E1} and C_{E2} _____ transient
signals to ground keeping them from appearing on
the emitters of Q1 and Q2, respectively.

⇲

bypass

What is the function of capacitors C_{E1} and C_{E2}?
_____
_____

⇲

to bypass transient sig-
nals to ground, keeping
them from appearing on
the emitters of Q1 and
Q2

354

MONOSTABLE MULTIVIBRATOR

⇩ A multivibrator is a triggered circuit usually consisting of _____ transistors.

two

⇩ In a multivibrator, when one transistor conducts the other is _____.

cut off

⇩ In a *monostable* multivibrator, one of the transistors is normally cut off, and the other transistor in a _____ multivibrator is normally conducting.

monostable

⇩ An input trigger pulse is required to change the transistors from their normal states in a _____ multivibrator.

monostable

⇩ Thus, a monostable multivibrator is triggered by an _____ trigger pulse.

input

⇩ The output of a monostable multivibrator is a square pulse. Thus, an input trigger pulse produces an output _____ pulse.

square

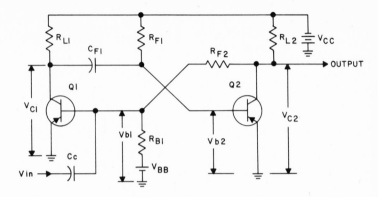

MONOSTABLE MULTIVIBRATOR

Figure 14

The circuit in Figure 14 is a monostable multivibrator. The input trigger is applied to the base of transistor

▽ _____.

Q1

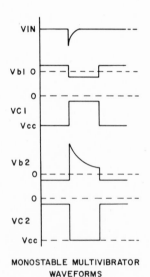

MONOSTABLE MULTIVIBRATOR
WAVEFORMS

Figure 15

As illustrated in Figure 15 the input trigger used in this circuit is a _____ (positive, negative)

▽ spike pulse.

negative

356

A negative voltage on the base of Q1, a P-N-P transistor, creates a _____ bias on the emitter-base junction.

▽

forward

Thus, a negative spike pulse applied to the base of Q1 will cause Q1 to _____.

▽

conduct

If an input trigger (negative spike pulse) is required to enable Q1 to conduct this transistor is normally

▽ _____.

cut off

In the circuit shown in Figure 14, transistor _____ is normally cut off and _____ is normally conducting.

▽

Q1
Q2

A negative input spike pulse applied to the circuit will cause Q1 to _____ and Q2 to

▽ _____.

conduct
cut off

According to Figures 14 and 15, before Q1 conducts, its collector voltage is approximately equal to

▽ _____.

— V$_{CC}$ (supply voltage)

When Q1 conducts, electron current flows _____ (into, out of) the collector.

▽

into

357

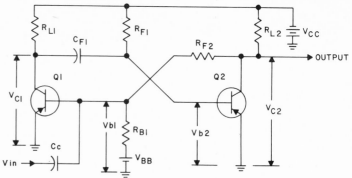

MONOSTABLE MULTIVIBRATOR

Figure 14

When Q1 conducts, electron current flows through resistor R_{L1}, causing the collector of Q1 to become _____ (more, less) negative or _____ (more, less) positive.

less
more

When Q1 conducts, its collector voltage _____ (increases, decreases) in the positive direction.

increases

This positive change in voltage is coupled through capacitor C_{F1} to the _____ of Q2.

base

This positive change creates a _____ voltage at the base of Q2.

positive (higher)

A positive voltage at the base of Q2 creates a bias in the _____ direction on the emitter-base junction.

reverse

358

A reverse bias on the emitter-base junction of Q2
⇨ causes this transistor to _____.

cut off

A positive change at the collector of Q1 when Q1
conducts is coupled to the base of Q2, causing Q2
⇨ to _____.

cut off

When Q2 cuts off, its collector voltage approaches
⇨ _____.

$- V_{\text{CC}}$ *(supply voltage)*

A negative voltage appearing at the collector of Q2
also appears at the base of Q1, keeping Q1 in the
⇨ _____ state.

conduction

As Q1 goes into conduction, the capacitor C_{F1} begins
⇨ to _____.

discharge

As capacitor C_{F1} discharges, the discharge current
⇨ through R_{F1} _____ (increases, decreases).

decreases

As the current through R_{F1} decreases the voltage
⇨ drop across R_{F1} _____.

decreases

Thus, as the voltage across C_{F1} decreases, the voltage
at the base of Q2 becomes _____ (more,
⇨ less) positive.

less

359

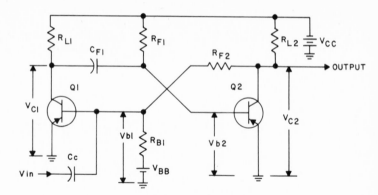

MONOSTABLE MULTIVIBRATOR

Figure 14

◇ As the voltage at the base of Q2 is decreased, the bias in the _____ direction is decreased.

reverse

◇ When the voltage at the base of Q2 has decreased far enough, transistor Q2 will again _____.

conduct

◇ Thus, when capacitor C_{F1} has discharged to a certain level, transistor Q2 will _____.

conduct

◇ When Q2 conducts, its collector voltage becomes less _____ (negative, positive) or more _____.

negative
positive

◇ A change in voltage at the collector of Q2 appears at the _____ of Q1.

base

▽ A positive rise in voltage at the collector of Q2 appears at the _____ of _____.

base
Q1

▽ A positive rise in the voltage at the base of Q1, which is a P-N-P transistor, will increase the bias in the _____ direction at the emitter-base junction.

reverse

▽ A reverse bias on the emitter-base junction of Q1 will cause Q1 to _____.

cut off

▽ When Q2 goes into conduction, the positive rise in voltage at its collector appears at the base of Q1, causing Q1 to _____.

cut off

▽ Before Q1 can again conduct, another _____ has to be applied to the base of Q1.

trigger (input spike pulse,
negative spike)

▽ After another input trigger has been applied and Q1 is again conducting, capacitor C_{F1} is _____.

discharging

▽ As C_{F1} discharges, the voltage at the base of Q2 _____, causing the reverse bias on the emitter-base junction of Q2 to _____.

decreases
decrease

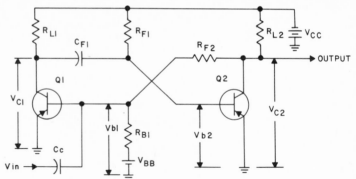

MONOSTABLE MULTIVIBRATOR

Figure 14

The rate at which the reverse bias on the emitter-base junction of Q2 decreases is determined by the rate at which capacitor _____ discharges.

C_{F1}

Thus, the time at which Q2 returns to the conduction state is determined by the discharge rate of capacitor _____.

C_{F1}

The output of this multivibrator is taken from the _____ of Q2.

collector

The output of this multivibrator is determined by the state of transistor _____, i.e., conducting or cut off.

Q2

When Q2 is conducting, the output is _____ than when Q2 is cut off.

higher (more positive, less negative)

362

For a negative spike pulse input, this multivibrator
produces a negative _____ pulse output.

square

This negative square pulse output is produced when
Q2 is _____.

cut off

The length of time Q2 is cut off is determined by
capacitor _____.

C_{F1}

Thus, the width of the negative square pulse output
is determined by capacitor _____.

C_{F1}

The circuit in Figure 14 is a _____ multivibrator in which an input consisting of a negative
_____ pulse produces a negative _____
pulse output.

monostable
spike (trigger)
square

set **9**

BISTABLE MULTIVIBRATOR

A *bistable* multivibrator requires an input trigger pulse for *each* change of state. A multivibrator which requires an input trigger pulse to change its state ⟁ from any previous state is _____.

bistable

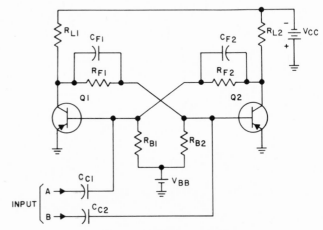

CONVENTIONAL BISTABLE MULTIVIBRATOR

Figure 16

The circuit in Figure 16 is a bistable multivibrator. It requires _____ (0, 1, 2) trigger pulse (s) for *each* change of state. It requires _____ (0, 1, 2, 3, 4) trigger pulse (s) for four changes of ⟁ state.

1

4

In this circuit the input trigger pulses are applied at ⟁ the _____ of the transistors.

bases

364

In the quiescent state either of the transistors may be conducting while the other is _____.

cut off

In order to change the state of a given transistor, a trigger pulse of the correct polarity must be introduced to the _____ of that transistor.

base

In the circuit shown in Figure 16, for a P-N-P transistor that is initially cut off, a _____ (positive, negative) trigger pulse must be introduced to its base.

negative

A negative pulse creates a _____ (forward, reverse) bias causing the transistor to conduct.

forward

This causes the collector voltage of this transistor to _____ (increase, decrease) in the positive direction.

increase

This positive rise is coupled to the base of the other transistor causing the transistor to _____.

cut off

A negative trigger pulse applied to the base of a cutoff transistor causes that transistor to _____ and the resulting positive rise in its collector voltage is coupled to the base of the conducting transistor, causing it to _____.

conduct
cut off

The output waveform may be taken from the collector of either _____.

⟁   *transistor*

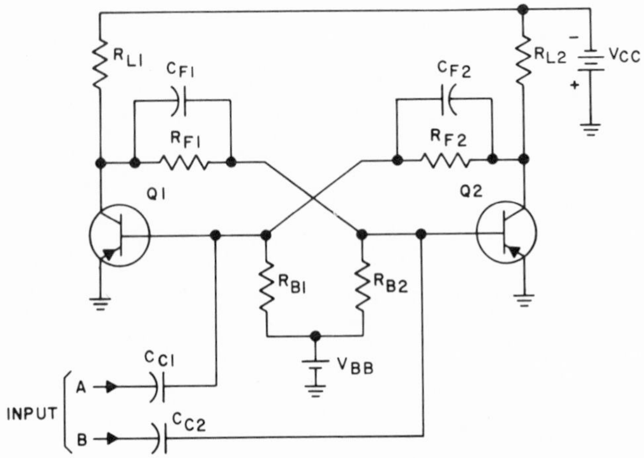

CONVENTIONAL BISTABLE MULTIVIBRATOR

Figure 16

The collector voltage of a transistor that is cut off is approximately equal to _____ (Figure 16). This supply voltage is _____ (positive, negative).

⟁

$-V_{CC}$ *(supply   voltage negative*

When the transistor goes into conduction, its collector voltage _____ (increases, decreases) in the positive direction, which is the same as a _____ in the negative direction.

⟁

increases
decrease

Thus, the output taken from the _____ of this transistor is a unit step voltage each time a correct input pulse is applied to the multivibrator.

⟁

collector

When this transistor goes into cutoff its collector voltage changes one unit step in the _____ direction and when it goes into conduction its collector voltage changes one unit step in the

⌵   _____ direction.

negative
positive

The output waveform of the other transistor is the inverse of the output waveform of this transistor. When one collector voltage increases one unit step,

⌵   the other _____ one unit step.

decreases

The output can be taken from either collector; one

⌵   waveform is the _____ of the other.

inverse (opposite polarity)

For a P-N-P transistor that is initially conducting, a _____ (positive, negative) trigger pulse is

⌵   required at its base in order to produce an output.

positive

A positive trigger pulse applied to the base of the conducting transistor creates a _____ bias

⌵   at the emitter-base junction.

reverse

This reverse bias causes that transistor to

⌵   _____ .

cut off

The resulting negative going voltage at the collector is coupled to the _____ of the other tran-

⌵   sistor, causing it to _____ .

base
conduct

367

When a positive input trigger pulse is applied to the base of a transistor that is initially conducting, that transistor is _____ and the resulting negative going collector voltage is coupled to the _____ of the other transistor causing it to

⇨

cut off
base
conduct

_____.

Should a negative input trigger pulse be applied to the base of a P-N-P transistor that is initially conducting, the forward bias would be _____

⇨ (increased, decreased).

increased

This would cause the transistor to be driven further into the _____ (conducting, nonconducting)

⇨ state.

conducting

The collector voltage of this transistor _____

⇨ (would, would not) go more negative.

would not

In this case a forward bias _____ (would, would not) appear at the emitter-base junction of the initially nonconducting transistor and that transistor

⇨ _____ (would, would not) change state.

would not
would not

A negative trigger pulse applied to a transistor that is _____ would not change the state of the

⇨ multivibrator.

conducting

Similarly, in a transistor that is initially cut off, a
_____ (positive, negative) trigger pulse applied to its base would not change that state of the
multivibrator.

positive

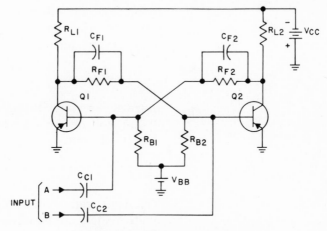

CONVENTIONAL BISTABLE MULTIVIBRATOR

Figure 16

In order for the bistable multivibrator in Figure 16
to operate, a _____ trigger input pulse must
be applied to the conducting transistor or a
_____ trigger input pulse must be applied
to the cutoff transistor.

positive
negative

set **10 PULSE STEERING**

In bistable multivibrators, a trigger input pulse of the correct polarity must be applied to the _____
⇡ of the correct transistor for circuit operation.

base

In triggering multivibrators, pulses of the same polarity are most often used. The input trigger pulses are
⇡ usually all positive or all _____.

negative

The input trigger pulses used in triggering bistable
⇡ multivibrators are usually of the same _____.

polarity

Switching time is delayed if the input trigger pulse is applied to both transistors simultaneously. Simultaneous application of the input trigger to both tran-
⇡ sistors causes delay in _____.

switching time

To prevent _____ in switching time it is desirable to apply the input trigger only to the proper
⇡ transistor.

delay

Applying the input trigger to only the proper transistor of a bistable multivibrator causes switching to
⇡ be _____ (faster, slower).

faster

370

It is desirable to apply the trigger to first one and then the other transistor when a pulse of the
_____ (same, opposite) polarity is used for
⟱ each trigger.

same

Trigger pulse steering is the process of steering the
⟱ _____ to the correct transistor.

trigger pulse (input trigger)

A process of directing an input trigger to the proper
⟱ transistor is called _____.

trigger pulse steering (input trigger steering)

One method of trigger pulse steering is by the use of
diodes. This method is sometimes called
⟱ d_____ steering.

diode

⟱ Diode steering is a method of _____.

trigger pulse steering (steering trigger pulses)

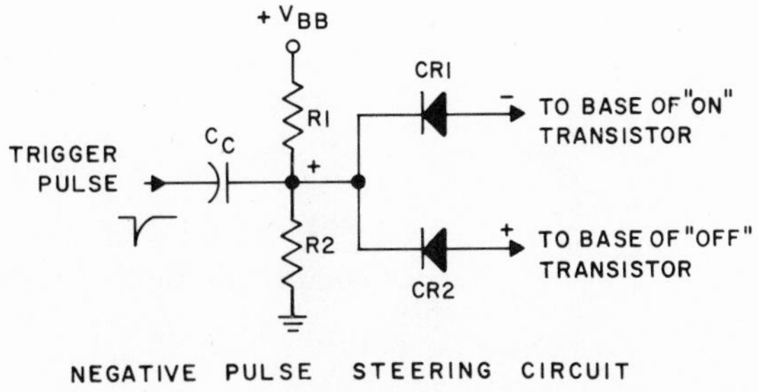

NEGATIVE PULSE STEERING CIRCUIT

Figure 17

Figure 17 illustrates a pulse steering circuit in which
⟱ _____ (positive, negative) pulses are used.

negative

371

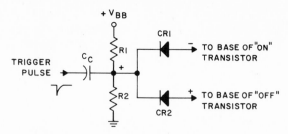

NEGATIVE PULSE STEERING CIRCUIT

Figure 17

This circuit is used to steer negative input
_____ to the proper transistor for bistable
multivibrator operation.

In this circuit, resistors R1 and R2 form a voltage
divider which divides the battery voltage. The battery voltage is _____.

The junction of R1 and R2 is maintained at a voltage
greater than 0 (ground) and less than _____.

The junction of R1 and R2 is maintained at a
_____ (positive, negative) potential.

The cathodes of diodes CR1 and CR2 are connected
to the junction of resistors _____ and
_____.

The cathodes of CR1 and CR2 are maintained at a
_____ (positive, negative) potential.

372

A requirement for diode conduction is that its plate (anode) be more _____ (positive, negative) than its cathode.

positive

In Figure 17, the voltage at the plate of a diode must be _____ (less than, greater than) the voltage at the junction of resistors R1 and R2 before the diode will conduct.

greater than

In this situation (the plate voltage higher than the cathode voltage) the diode is biased in the _____ direction.

forward

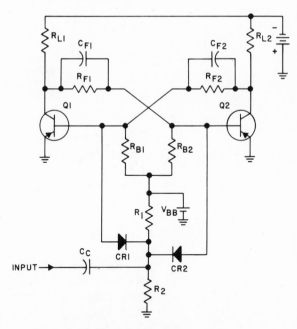

BISTABLE MULTIVIBRATOR WITH
NEGATIVE-PULSE STEERING DIODES

Figure 18

In Figure 18, the plates of CR1 and CR2 are connected to the _____ of transistors Q1 and Q2, respectively.

bases

373

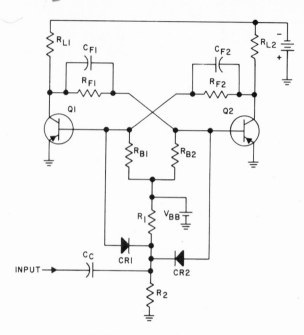

BISTABLE MULTIVIBRATOR WITH
NEGATIVE-PULSE STEERING DIODES

Figure 18

When a transistor in this circuit is conducting, its base voltage is _____ (high, low) and when a transistor is cut off, its base voltage is _____ (high, low).

low

high (positive)

Assuming Q2 to be conducting in Figure 18, its base voltage would be lower than the cathode voltage of CR2. CR2 _____ (would, would not) conduct when an input trigger pulse is applied. Q1, in this case, would be _____.

would not

cut off

374

The base voltage of Q1 would be higher than the cathode voltage of CR1. CR1 would _____ when an input trigger was applied.

conduct

Thus, the input trigger pulse would then be applied to the base of Q1, causing Q1 to _____.

conduct

In Figure 18, each time a negative input trigger pulse is applied, it is directed to the transistor in the _____ state.

cutoff

At the same time, the input trigger is prevented from reaching the base of the transistor in the _____ state.

conducting

The input trigger is applied to the transistors alternately, the transistors in each case being initially _____.

cut off

Assuming that the input trigger has just been applied to the base of Q1, this transistor will then _____.

conduct

The rising collector voltage of Q1 is coupled to the base of Q2, causing Q2 to _____.

cut off

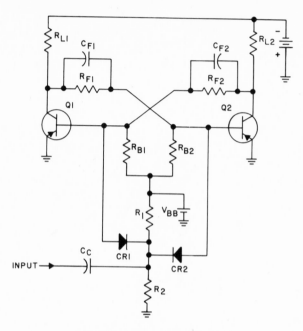

BISTABLE MULTIVIBRATOR WITH
NEGATIVE-PULSE STEERING DIODES

Figure 18

Since the voltage at the base of Q2 is now higher than the voltage at the junction of R1 and R2, diode CR2 _____ (will, will not) allow the next input trigger to appear at the base of Q2.

⌁ *will*

When this next input trigger occurs, diode _____ will conduct.

⌁ *CR2*

When this next input trigger occurs, it will appear at the base of transistor _____, causing it to conduct.

⌁ *Q2*

In diode steering, biasing of the diodes depends on the states of the _____ in the multivibrator circuit.

transistors

In the type of multivibrator in Figure 18, when *positive,* rather than negative, input trigger pulses are used, the diodes are situated and biased so that the positive trigger pulses will be applied to the bases of the transistors, which are initially _____.

conducting

The transistor which is initially conducting will then be _____.

cut off

Trigger pulse steering is the directing of the _____ to the proper transistors in the _____ multivibrator circuit to change the state of the multivibrator.

input trigger pulses
bistable

set **SCHMITT MULTIVIBRATOR**

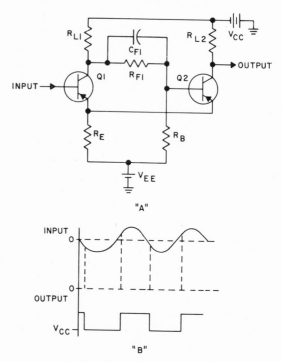

"A"

"B"

SQUARING CIRCUIT (SCHMITT TRIGGER)

Figure 19

⟡ Figure 19 is a squaring circuit. As the name indicates, its purpose is to _____ a pulse.

square

⟡ This squaring circuit is also referred to as a Schmitt Trigger circuit. It will change a sine wave to a _____ wave.

square

378

The Schmitt Trigger circuit is another version of a multivibrator and its purpose is to provide a
⎔ _____ in the output.

square wave

As the name of the Schmitt Trigger circuit implies, an input pulse must be present to _____ the circuit. In the absence of an input pulse, the circuit state remains unchanged.
⎔

trigger

The input to a Schmitt Trigger circuit could be a square wave, a sine wave, or any other shaped pulse, but the output will always be a _____.
⎔

square wave

The squaring circuit in Figure 19, generally referred to as a _____ circuit, is another version of a multivibrator whose output is a _____ regardless of the shape of the input pulse.
⎔

Schmitt Trigger
square wave

The Schmitt Trigger circuit is another version of a
⎔ m_____ .

multivibrator

As in other multivibrators, one section is conducting, while the other is _____.
⎔

cut off (nonconducting)

With no signal input, the right section is conducting and the left _____.
⎔

cut off (nonconducting)

379

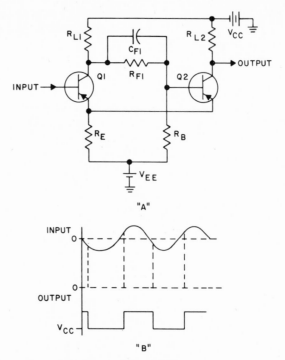

"A"

"B"

SQUARING CIRCUIT (SCHMITT TRIGGER)

Figure 19

A signal of proper amplitude will cause the left transistor to conduct. Conduction of the left transistor will, through multivibrator action, _____ the right transistor.

cut off

Multivibrator action is referred to as the simultaneous switching of the two sections of a multivibrator into opposite states. One transistor goes into _____, while the other is _____.

conduction
cut off

Figure 19 is a Schmitt circuit. In quiescent condition, the right transistor is conducting and the left

⟳ _____.

cut off

A signal at the left transistor will raise the transistor above cutoff. The left transistor is now _____ and, by multivibrator action, causes the right transistor

⟳ to be _____.

conducting
cut off

This condition will last until the signal goes down to a level at which the right transistor cannot be kept in cutoff. At this level the right transistor will start conducting and, by multivibrator action, _____

⟳ the left transistor.

cut off

The transistors have returned to the original state and will stay in the quiescent condition until the signal at the left transistor reaches a level which raises the transistor above cutoff. At this point, the transistor starts

⟳ _____ and the process is repeated.

conducting

This circuit uses direct coupling between the collector of the first transistor and base of the second transistor. The change in voltage across a resistor is instantaneous. The change from cutoff to conducting state and back again does not depend on the discharge of a capacitor.

⟳ *Proceed to the next frame.*

The width of the output pulse depends on the width of the input pulse. If the input pulse becomes narrower, the output pulse will also become _____, and if the input pulse becomes wider, the output pulse becomes _____.

Regardless of the shape of the input pulse, the output pulse will be a _____ and the width of the output pulse will follow the _____ of the _____.

The Schmitt Trigger circuit is a squaring circuit in which the width of the output pulse does not depend on the charge or _____ of a capacitor.

Having no built-in time constant, the width of the output pulse depends solely on the width of the _____.

A multivibrator whose sections are capacitor-coupled require a certain time to flip. Before the cutoff section can conduct, the coupling capacitor must _____ or _____.

Since the Schmitt Trigger circuit has direct coupling, the width of the output pulse _____ (does, does not) depend on a time constant. A capacitor _____ (is, is not) in the circuit for charge or discharge to permit the circuit to flip or flop.

◇

does not
is not

The Schmitt Trigger or squaring circuit has an output pulse of a _____ shape. In order to flip or flop, it does not depend on a _____ constant. The width of the output pulse depends solely on the _____ pulse and not on a capacitor _____ or _____.

◇

square
time
input
charge(ing)
discharge(ing)

PART SEVEN

LOGIC AND GATING CIRCUITS

Figures 3, 4, 5, 6, 7, and 10 in this part were reproduced with permission from E. Bukstein, "Computer Logic Circuits," Electronics World (January 1961) pp. 46, 47.

LOGIC CIRCUIT ANALYSIS

Logic circuits can be analyzed most efficiently and effectively if a systematic procedure of investigation is followed. An initial investigation of the circuit should determine whether the transistors are of the

↶ _____ or _____ type.

N-P-N
P-N-P

The first step in analyzing a logic circuit is to deter-
↶ mine the transistor _____.

type

After the transistor type has been established you should determine whether its elements are forward
↶ or _____ biased.

reverse

The second step in analyzing a logic circuit is to determine whether the transistor elements are
↶ _____ or _____ biased.

forward
reverse

The first two steps in analyzing a logic circuit are:
↶ (1) _____. (2) _____.

(1) determine the transis-
tor type
(2) determine the bias

If the emitter of a transistor is forward biased, it will be in the _____ (conducting, nonconducting) condition.

conducting

If a reverse bias is applied to the emitter and the transistor is cut off, the transistor _____ (is, is not) conducting.

is not

Forward bias on the emitter will cause the transistor to _____ heavily. A large reversed bias will _____ off the transistor and place it in the _____ condition.

conduct
cut
nonconducting (cutoff)

The third step is to determine the quiescent condition of the circuit. Check whether the transistor is in the _____ or _____ condition.

conducting
nonconducting (cutoff)

In a common-emitter circuit, bias is applied to the base. A negative bias on the base creates _____ (positive, negative) bias on the emitter with respect to the base, and a positive bias on the base is equivalent to a _____ bias on the emitter.

positive
negative

A negative bias on the base of an N-P-N transistor is equivalent to a positive bias on the emitter which constitutes _____ (forward, reverse) bias.

reverse

388

Biasing the base of an N-P-N transistor negatively is equivalent to biasing the emitter _____ and constitutes _____ bias. Under these conditions, the conduction of the transistor will be reduced or, if the bias is large enough, cut off.

⇨

positively
reverse

In logic circuits, a transistor conducts either heavily at saturation or is cut off. There are only two states: A transistor is either at _____ or at _____.

⇨

saturation
cutoff

In logic circuits, a transistor is either at saturation or at cutoff. Therefore when forward biased the transistor will conduct at _____ and when reverse biased the transistor will be at _____.

⇨

saturation
cutoff

The fourth step is to determine the voltage level of the collector with respect to the supply voltage when the circuit is in the quiescent state.

⇨ *Proceed to the next frame.*

A transistor in the nonconducting state _____ (will, will not) be at the same level voltage, whereas a transistor in the conducting state _____ (will, will not) be at the same level as the supply voltage.

⇨

will
will not

A circuit in quiescent state, having forward bias at the emitter, will be at _____ (saturation, cutoff) and will have a collector voltage _____ (equal to, different from) the supply voltage.

saturation
different from

To produce a signal in a circuit which is at saturation and has a low voltage level at the collector, the transistor must be cut off and the collector level _____ (lowered, raised).

raised

In order to raise the collector voltage level of transistor at saturation, the transistor must be _____.

cut off

An N-P-N transistor at saturation requires for cutoff an input signal of negative polarity applied to its base or a signal of _____ polarity applied to its emitter.

positive

For generating an output signal, an N-P-N transistor at saturation requires an input signal of _____ polarity applied to its base or of _____ polarity applied to its emitter.

negative
positive

An N-P-N transistor at saturation requires a
_____ signal applied to its emitter to cut it off
and to produce an output signal of _____
polarity. The collector voltage level will go from
_____ (high, low) to _____ (high,
☞ low).

positive
positive
low
high

The fifth step is to examine the complete circuit.
What effect will one signal have on the whole circuit? How many input signals are required for one
output? The circuit analysis will lead you to an
orderly understanding of a circuit function. Don't
be hasty. Follow step by step. Recheck your conclusions.

☞ *Proceed to next frame.*

In analyzing transistor logic circuits the first step is to
determine whether the transistors are of the
☞ _____ or _____ type.

N-P-N
P-N-P

After determining:
(1) the transistor type, and
(2) the bias on the various transistor elements,
examine whether the base-emitter potential makes
☞ the transistor forward or _____ biased.

reverse

391

Following the determination of
(1) the transistor type, and
(2) the biasing arrangement,
find the quiescent state of the transistor. Is the transistor in the conducting or _____ condition?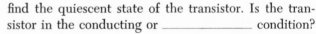

nonconducting or cutoff

After ascertaining
(1) transistor type,
(2) biasing arrangement, and
(3) quiescent condition of transistor,
check the voltage level of the collector in quiescent state. There are only two conditions, either high or

 _____ .

low

The next step after determining
(1) transistor type,
(2) biasing arrangement of emitter with respect to base,
(3) quiescent condition of transistor, and
(4) voltage level of collector,
draw your conclusions as to what effect a signal will have on the individual transistor and the whole circuit. This step will determine what circuit you are dealing with.

Proceed to next frame.

The five steps in transistor logic circuit analysis are:
(1) Determine the transistor *type*. Is it
    a _____ or _____?
(2) Examine the *bias* potential of emitter-base. Does
    it constitute _____ or _____
    bias?
(3) What is the *quiescent* condition of the transistor?
    Is the transistor _____ or _____?
(4) Determine voltage level *of collector*. Is it
    _____ or _____?
(5) What is the *effect of a signal* on the transistor
    and on the whole circuit? What circuit is it?

(1) N-P-N, P-N-P
(2) forward, reverse
(3) conducting (satura-
tion), nonconducting (cut
off)
(4) high, low

Give five steps for analyzing a logic circuit.
(1) _____
(2) _____
(3) _____
(4) _____
(5) _____

(1) Determine type of
transistor.
(2) Determine the bias
conditions.
(3) Determine quiescent
conditions.
(4) Determine voltage
level at collector.
(5) Determine the effect
of a signal on the circuit

set **2** ## "AND" AND "OR" CIRCUITS

An AND circuit requires an input signal to each input terminal to obtain the output. If a circuit has three input terminals, _____ (how many?) input signals are required for the circuit output.

▽

three

In an AND circuit having three input terminals, a signal must be applied to the first, AND to the second, AND to the third input terminal to receive an output. Therefore it is called a(n) _____

▽ circuit.

AND

Would you say that input signals must be supplied to *all* input terminals of an AND circuit to obtain an

▽ output signal? _____

Yes. All terminals must be fed input signals.

If one input terminal does not receive a signal, the AND circuit _____ (will, will not) have an

▽ output.

will not

In an AND circuit, all input terminals must receive input signals. All signals must appear at the same time to obtain an output signal. In other words, there must be *coincidence* of input signals. Therefore, an AND circuit is also referred to as a(n) _____

▽ circuit.

coincidence

Coincident input signals, or simultaneous input signals, mean that a signal is applied to input 1 AND input 2 AND input 3 AND to as many inputs as there are, all at the same time. A coincidence circuit is the same as a(n) _____ circuit.

⇨ *AND*

E_{IN}

"AND" CIRCUIT

Figure 1

⇨ *open*

The switches in Figure 1, are connected in series and shown in the _____ (open, closed) position.

⇨ *will not*

Since the circuit is open, the lamp _____ (will, will not) light.

⇨ *three (all)*

In order to close the circuit _____ (how many?) switches must be closed.

⇨ *will not*

If at least one switch is open, the lamp _____ (will, will not) light.

⇨ *coincidence*
output

To obtain an output signal, an AND circuit requires simultaneous inputs to each input terminal. There must be *coincidence* of all input signals to generate an output signal. Without _____ of all input signals, there is no _____ signal.

Because coincidence of all input signals is required to obtain an output, an AND circuit is also referred ▽ to as a(n) _____ circuit.

coincidence

▽ A coincidence circuit is a(n) _____ circuit.

AND

An AND circuit requires simultaneous input signals to obtain an output. If one input is missing, there ▽ _____ (will, will not) be an output.

will not

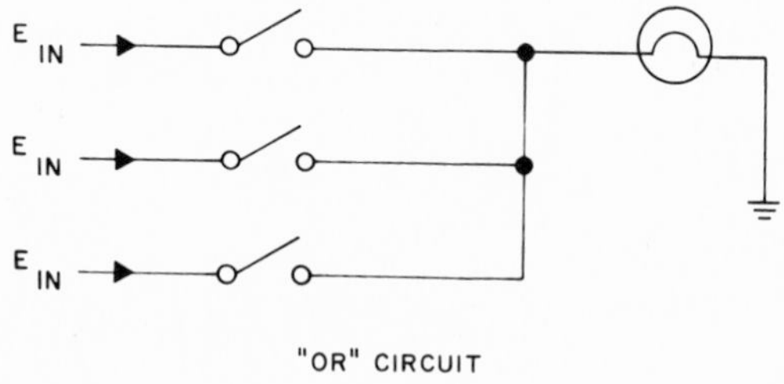

"OR" CIRCUIT

Figure 2

The switches in Figure 2 are connected in parallel and shown in the _____ (open, closed) ▽ position.

open

With all three switches open, current _____ (will, will not) flow and the lamp _____ ▽ (will, will not) light.

will not
will not

When the first switch is closed, the lamp ▽ _____ (will, will not) light.

will

If instead of closing the first switch, we close the second switch or the third switch or any combination of the switches, the lamp _____ (will, will not) light.

will

In an OR circuit each input signal will cause a signal to appear in the output. Not only each but also all input signals will generate an output signal. Therefore, coincidence of input signals _____ (is, is not) necessary.

is not

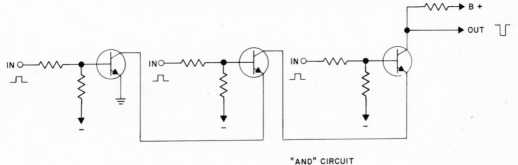

"AND" CIRCUIT

Figure 3

In analyzing the circuit of Figure 3, the type of transistor should be determined first. The transistors in the above reference are of the _____ type.

N-P-N

In no instance should there be _____ bias on the collector.

forward

To cut off a P-N-P transistor, the reverse bias applied to the emitter must be of _____ polarity. To cut off an N-P-N transistor, the reverse bias applied to the emitter must be of _____ polarity.

negative
positive

397

Bias is referred to as the voltage on the emitter with respect to the base. If a positive voltage is applied to the base, then the emitter is _____ (positively, negatively) biased.

negatively

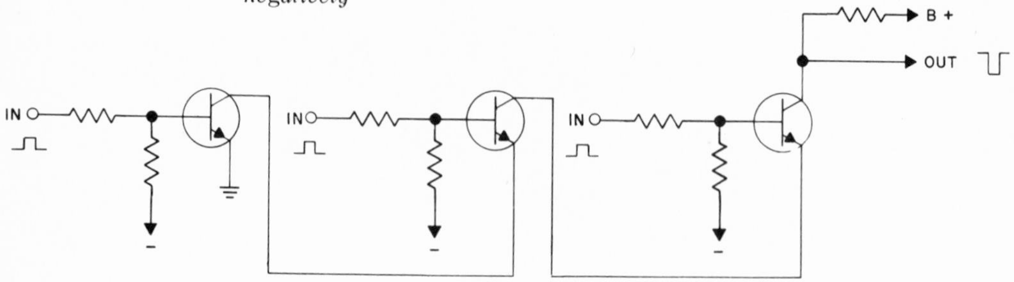

"AND" CIRCUIT

Figure 3

The emitters of the transistors in Figure 3 are positively, that is, _____ biased.

reverse

The transistors in Figure 3 are in series. Like switches, all must function correctly to permit a signal to go through. If one transistor does not act correctly the signal _____ (will, will not) go through.

will not

The symbols indicate that the transistors are of the _____ type. Application of a negative voltage to the base is the same as applying a _____ voltage to the emitter. The transistor is therefore biased in the _____ direction.

N-P-N
positive
reverse

398

Each base has a negative voltage. Therefore, each emitter is _____ biased with respect to the base.

⮿

positively (reverse)

A positive bias on the emitter of an N-P-N transistor is reverse biased. With no signal input, the transistors are at _____ and a signal _____ (will, will not) appear at the output.

⮿

cutoff
will not

If a large positive signal is applied to the base of one of the transistors, the transistor will conduct. The other transistors have not received an input signal and therefore _____ (will, will not) conduct.

⮿

will not

In order to obtain an ouput signal, three transistors must conduct because the transistors are connected in _____.

⮿

series

If large positive signals are applied to the bases of two (2) of the transistors, a signal _____ (will, will not) appear at the output.

⮿

will not

If large positive signals are applied to the bases of all three transistors, a signal _____ (will, will not) appear at the output.

⮿

will

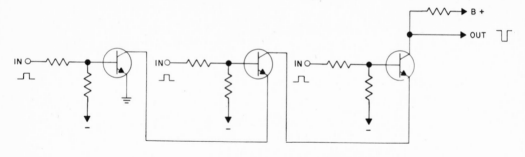

"AND" CIRCUIT

Figure 3

To obtain an output signal, an input signal
_____ (must, must not) be applied to each
transistor. In other words, an input signal
_____ (must, must not) be applied to the
first transistor AND to the second transistor AND
⟳ the third transistor.

must
must

Since an input signal must be applied to the first
AND the second AND the third transistor, this is
⟳ a(n) _____ circuit.

AND

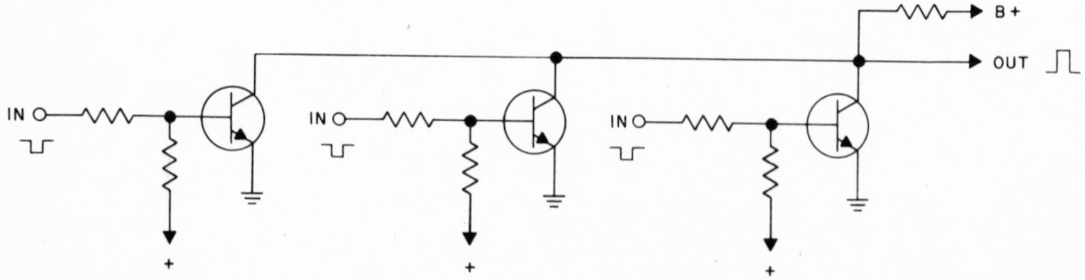

"AND" CIRCUIT

Figure 4

The collectors of the transistors in Figure 4 are tied
together. It can be said that they are connected in

⟳ _____.

parallel

400

Each base has a positive voltage which makes the emitter _____ biased with respect to the base.

negatively (forward)

The symbols indicate that the transistors are of the N-P-N type. A negative bias on the emitter of an N-P-N transistor represents _____ bias.

forward

With no signal input, all three transistors are conducting heavily and are close to saturation. If a large negative signal is applied to the base of one of the transistors, it will be cut off. Since the other two transistors are still conducting, a signal _____ (will, will not) appear at the output.

will not

If large negative signals appear on the bases of two transistors, they _____ (will, will not) be cut off and the signal _____ (will, will not) appear at the output.

will
will not

If large negative signals appear on the bases of all three transistors, they _____ (will, will not) be cut off and the signal _____ (will, will not) appear at the output.

will
will

Since input signals are required on the first AND second AND third transistor to obtain an output, this is a(n) _____ circuit.

AND

401

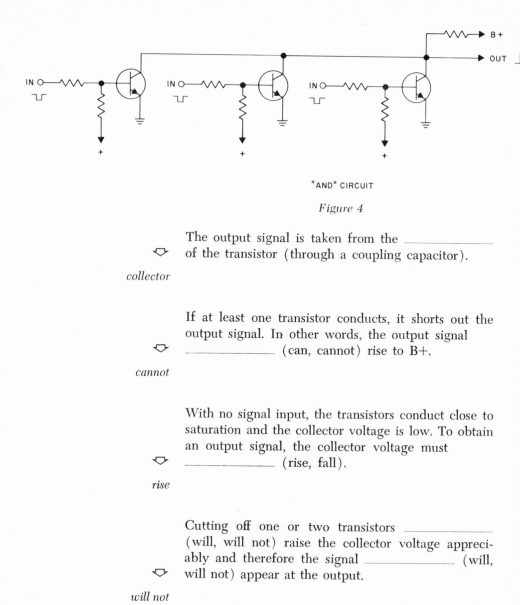

"AND" CIRCUIT

Figure 4

The output signal is taken from the _____ of the transistor (through a coupling capacitor).

collector

If at least one transistor conducts, it shorts out the output signal. In other words, the output signal _____ (can, cannot) rise to B+.

cannot

With no signal input, the transistors conduct close to saturation and the collector voltage is low. To obtain an output signal, the collector voltage must _____ (rise, fall).

rise

Cutting off one or two transistors _____ (will, will not) raise the collector voltage appreciably and therefore the signal _____ (will, will not) appear at the output.

will not
will not

If all transistors are cut off, the voltage _____ (will, will not) rise to B+ and the signal appears at the output.

will

402

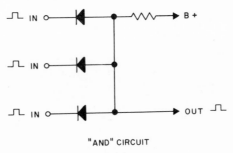

"AND" CIRCUIT

Figure 5

The plates of the diodes in Figure 5 are connected in _____ and B+ supplied to them through a resistor.

⊽ *parallel*

The cathodes are at ground potential and are therefore _____ (negative, positive) with respect to the plates.

⊽ *negative*

With no large positive signal at the cathode, the diodes _____ (will, will not) conduct.

⊽ *will*

If a large _____ (positive, negative) input signal appears at the cathode of one (1) diode, the diode will be cut off.

⊽ *positive*

With the condition of the previous frame in mind, will there be an appreciable change at the plates? _____

⊽ *No. The other two diode are still conducting heavily and the change at the plates will not be appreciable.*

403

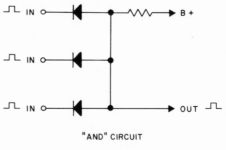

"AND" CIRCUIT

Figure 5

With no change of plate voltage, there _____

⟁ (will, will not) be a signal output.

will not

To obtain an output, _____ (how many?)
diodes must be _____. This would cause the

⟁ plate voltage to rise to _____.

all (all three)
cut off
B +

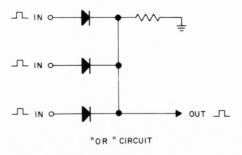

"OR" CIRCUIT

Figure 6

With three diodes connected to form an OR circuit,
as shown in Figure 6, there will be a signal at the
output if at least _____ (how many?)

⟁ diode(s) receive(s) an input.

one

The cathodes of the diodes are tied together and at ground potential. With no signal applied, the plates ✧ will also be at _____ potential.

ground

A diode can conduct only if the plate is at a _____ (higher, lower) potential than the ✧ cathode.

higher

If a positive signal is applied to the plate of one diode, a potential difference is created across the circuit since the plate now becomes _____
positive (positive, negative).

✧

With the plate positive, the diode conducts and develops a voltage of _____ polarity across ✧ the resistor.

positive

Thus, when a positive signal is applied to the plate of one diode an output _____ (will, will not) ✧ occur.

will

Figure 6 is a(n) _____ circuit since an input signal to the first diode _____ (AND, OR) the second diode _____ (AND, OR) ✧ the third diode will produce an output.

OR
OR
OR

405

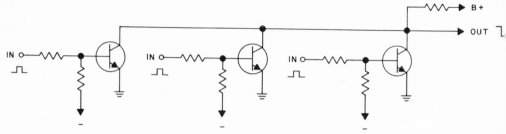

"NOR" CIRCUIT

Figure 7

In Figure 7, a large positive input signal applied to any transistor will raise that transistor from the cutoff condition into the _____ condition.

conducting (saturation)

With the transistor conducting, the voltage at the collector will go down and generate a _____ (negative, positive) going output signal.

negative

Suppose two transistors receive input signals at the same time. Would you expect to obtain two signals at the output? _____

No, of course not.

Whether one, two, or three signals appear simultaneously at the inputs, a signal is generated in the output circuit. Thus, this is a(n) _____ circuit.

OR

A circuit having a positive input but a negative output is said to *invert* the signal. This is also true if the input is negative and the output positive. It is therefore quite proper to call it a(n) _____ circuit.

inverter

406

If a negative input is applied to a(n) _____ circuit, the output is positive.

↪ *inverter*

In computer language, an inverter is called a NOT circuit. If a positive input is applied to a NOT circuit, the output is _____.

↪ *negative*

Give two names which we have mentioned for a circuit in which a positive input produces a negative output.

(1) _____.   (2) _____.

↪ *NOT*
inverter

There is a certain logic in naming an inverter a *NOT* circuit. If the input signal is called A, the output of an inverter is, without doubt, not the same, i.e., *not* A. This is therefore a(n) _____ circuit.

↪ *NOT (inverter)*

Depending upon whether a NOT circuit has the general characteristics of an AND or an OR circuit, it is called an NAND or a NOR circuit, respectively. An OR circuit with positive input and negative output becomes a(n) _____ circuit.

↪ *NOR*

An AND circuit with positive input and negative output becomes a(n) _____ circuit. An AND circuit with negative input and positive output becomes a(n) _____ circuit.

↪ *NAND*
NAND

407

Signal inversion and general properties of an AND circuit characterize the _____ circuit.

NAND

An OR circuit with signal inversion becomes a(n) _____ circuit. If the input is positive, the output is _____, and vice versa.

NOR
negative

Signal inversion and general properties of an OR circuit are the characteristics of a(n) _____ circuit.

NOR

A NOT circuit _____ the signal. If a NOT circuit has the general properties of an AND circuit, it becomes a(n) _____ circuit. If a NOT circuit has the general properties of an OR circuit, it becomes a(n) _____ circuit.

inverts
NAND
NOR

In reviewing the AND circuit, we can state this circuit will provide an output only if simultaneous input signals appear at _____ (how many?) input terminals.

all

If _____ (how many?) input signal(s) be missing, an output signal _____ (will, will not) be obtained.

one or more (any)
will not

408

An OR circuit has the property of requiring only one signal for obtaining an output. Suppose, two or three signals are applied to a multiple input circuit. Would you still expect an output? And how about signals to all inputs?

This was only a rhetorical question. By now, you certainly know that any additional input does not change the output.

Contrasting the AND with the OR circuit, we can state that the AND circuit requires input signals to _____ input terminals, while the OR circuit needs only _____ input signal to obtain an output.

all
one

In an AND circuit, all input signals arriving at their respective input terminals must have a certain relationship; they must arrive _____.

simultaneously (at the same time, coincidentally)

409

set 3

LOGICAL REPRESENTATIVES, "AND" AND "OR" CIRCUITS

In an AND circuit signals must be applied to ________(how many?) input terminals to obtain an output signal.

all

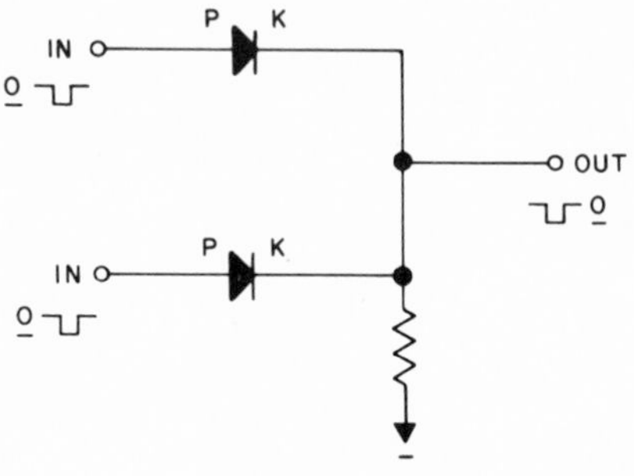

"AND" CIRCUIT

Figure 8

In Figure 8, the (K) terminals of the diodes are ________ biased.

negatively (forward)

With no negative signal input applied to the (P) terminals the diodes ________ (will, will not) conduct.

will

When both diodes conduct (no negative signal input) the output voltage is at ________ (zero, negative) potential, indicating no output signal.

zero

For an output signal to occur, the output potential must go ________.

negative

If a negative signal is applied to one input, its corresponding diode _____ (will, will not) ✧ conduct.

will not

When one diode does not conduct and the other does, the output signal is still at _____ potential, ✧ indicating no output signal.

zero (ground, the same)

When a negative signal is applied to both inputs, ✧ both diodes _____ (will, will not) conduct.

will not

When both diodes do not conduct, the output potential ✧ goes _____ indicating an output signal.

negative

In this circuit, _____ (how many?) input signal(s) are required for an output signal. This is ✧ a(n) _____ circuit.

both (2)
AND

An AND circuit may be represented by the logic symbol:

═╡ AND ╞═

A logic symbol for the circuit in Figure 8 is: (draw it)

✧

═╡ AND ╞═

411

In logic circuitry, whenever

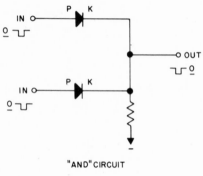

is encountered, we know this represents a(n) _____ circuit.

AND

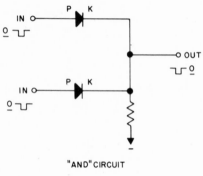

"AND" CIRCUIT

Figure 8

In logic circuitry, instead of using a detailed circuit such as Figure 8 to represent an AND circuit, the logic symbol (draw it)

may be used.

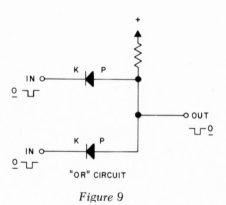

"OR" CIRCUIT

Figure 9

In Figure 9, the (P) terminals of the diodes are
_____ biased.

positively
(forward)

With no negative signal input, both diodes will conduct, holding the output at _____ potential,
indicating no output signal.

zero (ground)

When a signal is applied to one input terminal, the
corresponding diode conducts more heavily causing
the output potential to go _____ giving an
output signal.

negative

Similarly, when a negative signal is applied to the
other input terminal, the output potential goes
_____ producing an output signal.

negative

Also, when a negative signal is applied to both input
terminals, the output potential goes _____
producing an output signal.

negative

Thus an output signal appears when an input signal
is applied to one *or* the other *or* both input terminals.
This circuit is a(n) _____ circuit.

OR

A logic symbol for an OR circuit is:

$\dashv \boxed{\text{OR}} \vdash$

Figure 9 may be represented by the logic symbol:

$\dashv \boxed{\text{OR}} \vdash$ 413

In logic circuits, rather than use the detailed OR circuit, the logic symbol (draw it)

⟳ may be used in its place.

⊐ OR ⊢

Another logic symbol for an AND circuit is:

⊐ • ⊢

Two logic symbols for an AND circuit are:

and

⟳

⊐ AND ⊢

⊐ • ⊢

In some logic systems

⊐ AND ⊢

is used to represent _____ circuits, while in others the logic symbol (draw it)

⟳ may be used.

AND

⊐ • ⊢

⊐ OR ⊢ and ⊐ + ⊢

⟳ are logic symbols for _____ circuits.

OR

414

In addition to ⊣[OR]⊢

↔ is a logic symbol for an OR circuit.

⊣[+]⊢

In a logic system that uses

⊣[AND]⊢

to represent _____ circuits,

⊣[OR]⊢

↔ is used to represent _____ circuits.

AND
OR

Similarly in a logic system that uses

⊣[•]⊢

to represent _____ circuits,

↔ is used to represent OR circuits.

AND
⊣[+]⊢

The logic symbols,

⊣[AND]⊢ and ⊣[OR]⊢

_____ (would, would not) be used in the
↔ same logic system.

would

The logic symbols

⊣[+]⊢ and

↔ would be used in the same logic system.

⊣[•]⊢

415

Another logic symbol used to represent an AND circuit is:

$\exists \!\! \supset \!\! -$

The three logic symbols which are used to represent AND circuits are:

☞ (1)   (2)   (3)

(1) $\exists \!\! \supset \!\! -$

(2) $= \boxed{\text{AND}} -$

(3) $\exists \!\! \boxed{\;\bullet\;} \!\! -$

When

$\exists \!\! \supset \!\! -$

is used to represent a(n) _____ circuit,

$= \!\! \supset \!\! =$

☞ is used to represent an OR circuit.

AND

In logic system in which

$= \!\! \supset \!\! =$

represents a (n) _____ circuit,

☞ represents an AND circuit.

OR

$\exists \!\! \supset \!\! -$

416

Another logic symbol used to represent an OR circuit is:

⟹‍▷—

The four logic symbols for an OR circuit are:

(1)   (3)

▽ (2)   (4)

(1)   ⊐ OR ⊢

(2)   ⊐ + ⊢

(3)   ⊐⊃

(4)   ⟹▷—

When

⟹▷—

is used to represent a(n) _____ circuit,

⟹▷—

▽   is used to represent an AND circuit.

OR

In the same logic system,

⟹▷—

represents a(n) _____ circuit and

▽   represents an OR circuit.

AND

⟹▷—

417

$\dashv \boxed{\bullet} \vdash$ and $\Rightarrow\!\!\!\supset$-

are logic symbols used to represent _____

circuits.

Logic symbols for OR circuits corresponding to

$\dashv \boxed{\bullet} \vdash$ and $\Rightarrow\!\!\!\supset$-

are

and

respectively.

$\dashv \boxed{+} \vdash$

$\Rightarrow\!\!\!\!\Longrightarrow$-

The logic symbols

$\Rightarrow\!\!\!\!\triangleright$- and

would be used in the same logic system.

$\Rightarrow\!\!\!\!\triangleright$-

In a logic system that uses

$\Rightarrow\!\!\!\!\Longrightarrow$-

to represent a(n) _____ circuit,

$\Rightarrow\!\!\!\supset$-

is used to represent a(n) _____ circuit.

Four logic symbols used in representing AND circuits are

(1)   (3)

♢ (2)   (4)

(1)   ⊐ AND ⊢

(2)   ⊐ • ⊢

(3)   ⊐D⊢

(4)   ⊐▷⊢

set **4**

INHIBITOR CIRCUIT

As its name indicates, an inhibitor inhibits a circuit from functioning. This circuit is used in computers to *control* the output of a circuit. Therefore, an inhibitor has a _____ function.

▽

controlling

The simplest way to control the output is to control the *input*. An inhibitor is generally used to inhibit the _____ before it can cause an output.

▽

input

Inhibitor signals appearing at an input terminal will suppress or _____ the input signal. In doing so, an output signal _____ (will, will not) be present.

▽

inhibit (control)
will not

Provided that all other circuit requirements are fulfilled, the absence of an inhibitor signal will have no influence on the operation of an AND or OR circuit and a signal _____ (can, cannot) go through.

▽

can

To obtain an output signal in an AND circuit, two conditions must be fulfilled:
(1) all inputs must receive input signals simultaneously, and
(2) inhibitor signals must be _____ (present, absent).

▽

absent

For a signal to appear in the output of an AND circuit:

(1) _____ (how many?) inputs must receive input signals, and

(2) inhibitor signal must be _____ (present, absent).

▽

all
absent

An AND circuit will exhibit an output if two conditions exist:

(1) _____

(2) _____

▽

(1) all input signals must be present
(2) inhibitor signals must be absent

When an inhibitor signal is present, an AND circuit _____ (will, will not) exhibit an output even if all inputs receive input signals.

▽

will not

Suppose in an AND circuit there is no inhibitor signal but three out of four input signals are present. Would there be an output? _____

▽

Of course not — an AND circuit requires the presence of all input signals to obtain an output.

An OR circuit reacts to an inhibitor as follows: if an input signal and an inhibitor signal are simultaneously fed to an input, the inhibitor will cancel or _____ the input signal.

▽

inhibit

In an OR circuit an input signal, if not inhibited, will cause an output. Thus, each input to be inhibited must be sent through a(n) _____ circuit. Any other input _____ (will, will not) be

⇩ affected by an inhibitor signal.

inhibitor
will not

Computer people have a language and logic of their own. They say that an inhibitor has a NOT function
⇩ by cancelling or _____ a signal.

inhibiting (notting)

In the presence of an input signal an inhibitor signal acts like a N_____ circuit. To cancel, nullify, or inhibit the input signal, the inhibitor circuit output must be of the _____ (same, opposite)
⇩ polarity.

NOT
opposite

Assume that an input signal is fed to a circuit. The controlling or inhibitor circuit is triggered at the same
⇩ time and _____ the input signal.

inhibits (cancels, nullifies)

This action is the same as inverting the input signal. Since an inverter is called a NOT circuit, an inhibitor
⇩ is logically a type of _____ circuit.

NOT

In digital circuits, the signal voltage can be either high or _____ with respect to the quiescent
⇩ voltage level.

low

Thus, depending on the particular system, the quiescent condition could be considered either at a _____ or a _____ voltage level with respect to the signal voltage level.

⌖

low
high

Suppose the quiescent condition is at a low level voltage. The signal then will be at a _____

⌖ level voltage.

high

If the quiescent condition is at a high level voltage, the signal then will be at a _____ level voltage.

⌖ age.

low

An inhibitor, in order to inhibit or prevent an input signal, must produce a _____ level signal for a high level input signal and a _____

⌖ level signal for low level input signal.

low
high

To suppress or inhibit an input signal, the level of the inhibitor signal must be _____ (the

⌖ same as, opposite from) the input level.

opposite from

An inverter has an output opposite from the input. It is therefore called a NOT circuit. An inhibitor output signal is opposite from the signal it is designed to suppress or inhibit. By the same logic it is also

⌖ called a type of _____.

NOT circuit

423

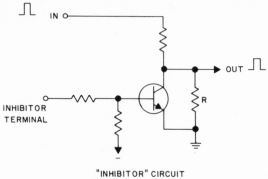

"INHIBITOR" CIRCUIT

Figure 10

Figure 10 illustrates an inhibitor which is a shunt circuit. As the name indicates, the input is ⌒ _____ to ground.

shunted

A transistor is connected across the resistor, R. The characteristic of an inhibitor is such that if no inhibitor signal is present at the inhibitor terminal, an input ⌒ signal _____ (can, cannot) go through.

can

The transistor is of the N-P-N type and the negative voltage on the base constitutes a reverse bias on the emitter. Thus, the transistor will be cut off with no inhibitor signal at its terminal. In this condition an input _____ (will, will not) be permitted ⌒ to appear across R.

will

The transistor which is the inhibitor _____ (must, must not) be in the conducting state to per- ⌒ mit an input signal to go through.

must not

A signal at the inhibit terminal will cause the transistor to conduct and _____ an input signal

⊽ to ground.

shunt (short)

The input signal is positive or at _____ (high,

⊽ low) level.

high

To suppress or inhibit a high level input signal, the inhibitor must produce a _____ (high, low)

⊽ level signal.

low

With the transistor conducting, the collector is at _____ (low, high) level and an input signal normally appearing across R will be _____

⊽ to ground.

low
shunted

A high level input to be suppressed or inhibited should result in a signal of opposite level. This is the same as inverting the signal. Therefore an inhibitor

⊽ is logically a type of _____ circuit.

NOT (inverter)

LOGICAL REPRESENTATION, "NOT" AND INHIBITION CIRCUITS

A *NOT AND* circuit is an AND circuit whose output signal is inverted with respect to its input signals. An AND circuit whose input signals are negative but whose output signal is at ground level is a
⟿ _____ circuit.

NOT AND

A common name for a NOT AND circuit is a *NAND* circuit. The NOT AND circuit described in the previous frame could be called a(n) _____
⟿ circuit.

NAND

Since

represents a(n) _____ circuit,

represents a(n) _____ circuit.
⟿

AND
NAND

Instead of using a detailed NAND circuit in logic circuitry, the logic symbol

⟿ may be used.

426

An OR circuit in which the output signal is inverted
with respect to the input signal is called a
⟡ _____ OR or NOR circuit.

NOT

A more common name for a NOT OR circuit is a(n)
⟡ _____ circuit.

NOR

The logic symbol,

⊐▭NOR▭⊐

⟡ represents a _____ circuit.

NOR

The symbol,

represents a NOR circuit, and the symbol

⟡ represents a NAND circuit.

⊐▭NOR▭⊐

⊐▭NAND▭⊐

In the same logic system

⊐▭NAND▭⊐

represents a _____ circuit and

⟡ represents a NOR circuit.

NAND

⊐▭NOR▭⊐

427

When a signal is applied to the *inhibit terminal* an inhibitor circuit _____ (will, will not) produce an output signal.

▽

will not

The signal which inhibits in an inhibitor circuit is applied at the _____ terminal.

▽

inhibit

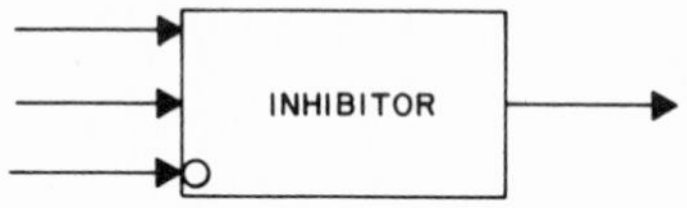

LOGIC SYMBOL FOR INHIBITOR CIRCUIT

Figure 11

The logic symbol in Figure 11 represents a(n) _____ circuit.

▽

inhibitor

In this symbol for an inhibitor circuit the inhibit signal is applied to the input designated by a small circle. This is the _____ terminal.

▽

inhibit

The inhibitor circuit can be called an *AND-NOT* circuit. Figure 11 represents an inhibitor or a(n) _____ circuit.

▽

AND-NOT

428

One logic symbol for an inhibitor circuit is

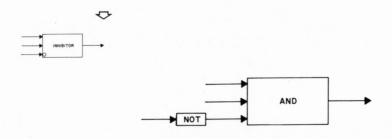

LOGIC SYMBOL FOR AND NOT (INHIBITOR) CIRCUIT

Figure 12

Another logic symbol for the inhibitor or AND-NOT circuit is shown in Figure 12. Two logic symbols for an inhibitor or AND-NOT circuit are

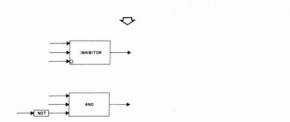

and

In Figure 12, an AND-NOT or inhibitor circuit is the same as an AND circuit with one input inverted. This inverted input terminal is the _____ terminal.

inhibit

429

If you were to invert one input of a(n) _____ circuit, an inhibitor circuit would result.

AND

In an inhibitor or AND-NOT circuit the output signal is inhibited by a signal applied to the _____ terminal.

inhibit

Congratulations! You have just finished a programed course in Transistor Physics and Basic Circuit Applications. We hope that the knowledge you have gained from this course will prove beneficial to you in furthering your career in Electronics.